Houghton Mifflin

Math Expressions

Grade 5

Assessment Guide

Developed by
The Children's Math Worlds
Research Project

PROJECT DIRECTOR AND AUTHOR

Dr. Karen C. Fuson

This material is based upon work supported by the
National Science Foundatic
under Grant Numbers
ESI-9816320, REC-9806020, and RED-9

Any opinions, findings, and conclusions or recommenda
material are those of the author and do not necessarily r
National Science Foundation.

HOUGHTON MIFFLIN BOSTON

Teacher Reviewers

Kindergarten

Patti Sugiyama
Wilmette, Illinois

Barbara Wahle
Evanston, Illinois

Grade 1

Megan Rees
Chicago, Illinois

Sandra Budson
Newton, Massachusetts

Janet Pecci
Chicago, Illinois

Grade 2

Molly Dunn
Danvers, Massachusetts

Agnes Lesnick
Hillside, Illinois

Grade 3

Sandra Tucker
Chicago, Illinois

Jane Curran
Honesdale, Pennsylvania

Grade 4

Sara Stoneberg Llibre
Chicago, Illinois

Sheri Roedel
Chicago, Illinois

Grade 5

Todd Atler
Chicago, Illinois

Leah Barry
Norfolk, Massachusetts

Credits

Cover art: (stopwatch) © Photodisc/Getty Images. (cheetah) © John Daniels/Ardea London Ltd. (train) © Michael Dunning/Photographer's Choice/Getty Images.

Illustrative art: Schawk Inc.
Technical art: Schawk Inc.

Printed in the U.S.A.

ISBN-13: 978-0-618-58950-0
ISBN-10: 0-618-58950-3

1 2 3 4 5 6 7 8 9 DH 11 10 09 08 07 06

GRADE 5 ASSESSMENT GUIDE

TABLE OF CONTENTS

Student Record Sheet A1

Unit 1
- Quick Quiz 1 .... A2
- Quick Quiz 2 .... A3
- Quick Quiz 3 .... A4
- Unit Test Form A A5
- Unit Test Form B A7
- Performance Assessment A11

Mini Unit A
- Unit Test Form A A14
- Unit Test Form B A17
- Performance Assessment A21

Unit 2
- Quick Quiz 1 .... A24
- Quick Quiz 2 .... A25
- Quick Quiz 3 .... A26
- Quick Quiz 4 .... A27
- Unit Test Form A A28
- Unit Test Form B A30
- Performance Assessment A34

Mini Unit B
- Unit Test Form A A37
- Unit Test Form B A39
- Performance Assessment A41

Unit 3
- Quick Quiz 1 .... A44
- Quick Quiz 2 .... A44
- Quick Quiz 3 .... A45
- Unit Test Form A A46
- Unit Test Form B A48
- Performance Assessment A50

Mini Unit C
- Unit Test Form A A53
- Unit Test Form B A55
- Performance Assessment A57

Unit 4
- Quick Quiz 1 .... A60
- Quick Quiz 2 .... A60
- Quick Quiz 3 .... A61
- Quick Quiz 4 .... A61
- Unit Test Form A A62
- Unit Test Form B A64
- Performance Assessment A67

Mini Unit D
- Unit Test Form A A70
- Unit Test Form B A73
- Performance Assessment A76

Unit 5
- Quick Quiz 1 .... A79
- Quick Quiz 2 .... A79
- Quick Quiz 3 .... A80
- Unit Test Form A A81
- Unit Test Form B A83
- Performance Assessment A85

Mini Unit E
- Unit Test Form A A88
- Unit Test Form B A90
- Performance Assessment A93

Unit 6
- Quick Quiz 1 .... A96
- Quick Quiz 2 .... A98
- Quick Quiz 3 .... A99
- Unit Test Form A A100
- Unit Test Form B A102
- Performance Assessment A106

Mini Unit F
- Unit Test Form A A109
- Unit Test Form B A111
- Performance Assessment A114

Class Record Sheet

Unit ____

Name of Student	Unit Objectives								

Unit 1
Quick Quiz 1

Name ______________________ Date ____________

Solve each multiplication exercise.

1. $3 \times 8 =$ 24

2. $9 * 2 =$ 18

3. $7 \bullet 5 =$ 35

4. $5 \times 6 =$ 30

5. $6 \times 7 =$ 42

Solve each division exercise.

6. $24 \div 6 =$ 4

7. $36/4 =$ 9

8. $40 \div 8 =$ 5

9. $3\overline{)21}$ 7

10. $10 \div 5 =$ 2

Unit 1
Quick Quiz 2

Name ______ Date ______

Solve each multiplication exercise.

1. $8s = 32$
   $s =$ 4

2. $90 = 10x$
   $x =$ 9

3. $g = 56/7$
   $g =$ 8

Extend the function table.

4.

input	0	2	3	4	5	6
output	0	8	12	16	20	24

Write the rule for the function table.

5.

Rule: $p = 9t$					
teams (t)	1	2	3	4	5
players (p)	9	18	27	36	45

Unit 1
Quick Quiz 3

Name ______________________ Date ______________

Solve each equation.

1. $n = 27 - (\frac{35}{5})$

   $n =$ 20

2. $(263 \times 487) \times 952 = n \times (487 \times 952)$

   $n =$ 263

Solve.

Show your work.

3. Karie and Sanjay collect marbles. Sanjay has 11 marbles. Karie has 6 times as many marbles as Sanjay. How many marbles does Karie have?

   $11 \times 6 = 66$ marbles

4. Tina has saved 7 quarters. Each week her parents will give her 5 more quarters. How many quarters will Tina have after 4 weeks? $7 + (5 \times 4) = 27$ quarters

5. There are cows, horses, and ducks on a farm. There are half as many cows as horses on the farm. There are 6 times as many ducks as cows on the farm. If there are 45 animals altogether on the farm, how many of each kind of animal are on the farm?

   5 cows, 10 horses, and 30 ducks

Unit 1 Test
Form A

Name ______________________ Date __________

Solve each multiplication exercise.

1. $6 \times 7 =$ 42

2. $4 * 9 =$ 36

3. $8 \bullet 3 =$ 24

4. $7 \times 8 =$ 56

5. $2 \times 5 =$ 10

6. $9 * 2 =$ 18

7. $5 \bullet 6 =$ 30

Solve each division exercise.

8. $35 \div 7 =$ 5

9. $\frac{24}{3} =$ 8

10. $27 \div 9 =$ 3

11. $4\overline{)24} =$ 6

12. $56 \div 8 =$ 7

13. $\frac{18}{2} =$ 9

14. $6\overline{)12} =$ 2

Extend the function table.

15.

input	1	2	3	4	5	6
output	5	10	15	20	25	30

Write the rule for the function table.

16.

Rule: $l = 8s$					
spiders (s)	1	2	3	4	5
legs (l)	8	16	24	32	40

Name Date

Solve each equation.

17. $6r = 42$ 7

18. $40 = 10w$ 4

19. $50 \times 0 =$ 0

20. $f = 45 - (3 \bullet 5)$ 30

Use the Properties of Multiplication to solve for n.

21. $(335 \times 426) \times 205 = n \times (426 \times 205)$ 335

22. $1{,}598 \times 675 = n \times 1{,}598$ 675

Solve.

23. Clara and Eddy collect cans to recycle. Eddy has 12 cans. Clara has 4 times as many cans as Eddy. How many cans does Clara have?

$12 \times 4 = 48$ cans

24. Gino and Roger read as many books as they can. Roger reads 30 books. That is 5 times as many as Gino reads. How many books does Gino read?

$30 \div 5 = 6$ books

25. **Extended Response** Sally has a bag with red, blue, and green marbles. She has twice as many blue marbles as red marbles. She has 5 times as many green marbles as red marbles. Altogether she has 24 marbles. How many of each color marble does she have? Explain how you found your answer.

3 red, 6 blue, and 15 green marbles. If r is the number of red marbles, then the number of blue marbles equals $2r$ and the number of green marbles equals $5r$. So $r + 2r + 5r = 24$; $8r = 24$; $r = 3$. Sally has 3 red marbles, twice that is 6 blue marbles, and $5 \times 3 = 15$ green marbles.

Unit 1 Test
Form B

Name ____________________ Date __________

Fill in the circle for the correct answer.

Solve each multiplication exercise.

1. $3 \times 4 =$

Ⓐ 4
Ⓑ 8
Ⓒ 12
Ⓓ 34

2. $9 \bullet 8 =$

Ⓕ 98
Ⓖ 72
Ⓗ 64
Ⓚ 18

3. $6 * 2 =$

Ⓐ 6
Ⓑ 12
Ⓒ 18
Ⓓ 24

4. $8 \times 8 =$

Ⓕ 16
Ⓖ 56
Ⓗ 62
Ⓚ 64

5. $2 \bullet 7 =$

Ⓐ 14
Ⓑ 21
Ⓒ 27
Ⓓ 72

6. $5 \times 3 =$

Ⓕ 10
Ⓖ 12
Ⓗ 15
Ⓚ 53

7. $7 * 6 =$

Ⓐ 13
Ⓑ 35
Ⓒ 36
Ⓓ 42

Solve each division exercise.

8. $15 \div 3 =$

Ⓕ 5
Ⓖ 6
Ⓗ 12
Ⓚ 18

9. $81 \div 9 =$

Ⓐ 8
Ⓑ 9
Ⓒ 10
Ⓓ 72

10. $20 / 5 =$

Ⓕ 4
Ⓖ 5
Ⓗ 6
Ⓚ 15

Name Date

11. $56 \div 8 =$

Ⓐ 9
Ⓑ 8
Ⓒ 7
Ⓓ 6

12. $7\overline{)21} =$

Ⓕ 14
Ⓖ 7
Ⓗ 4
Ⓚ 3

13. 16 / 2 =

Ⓐ 18
Ⓑ 16
Ⓒ 9
Ⓓ 8

14. $6\overline{)36} =$

Ⓕ 16
Ⓖ 6
Ⓗ 7
Ⓚ 8

Which numbers extend this function table?

15.

input	1	2	3	4	5	6
output	6	12	18			

Ⓐ 24, 30, and 36 Ⓑ 20, 25, and 30 Ⓒ 19, 20, and 21 Ⓓ 14, 15, and 16

What is the rule for this function table?

16.

distance (d)	1	2	3	4	5
time (t)	7	14	21	28	35

Ⓕ $d = 7t$ Ⓖ $t = 6d$ Ⓗ $t = 7d$ Ⓚ $t = 7$

Name Date

Solve each equation.

17. $5p = 45$

Ⓐ $p = 8$ Ⓑ $p = 9$ Ⓒ $p = 10$ Ⓓ $p = 40$

18. $30 = 10q$

Ⓕ $q = 300$ Ⓖ $q = 20$ Ⓗ $q = 10$ Ⓚ $q = 3$

19. $12 \times 0 = r$

Ⓐ $r = 0$ Ⓑ $r = 1$ Ⓒ $r = 12$ Ⓓ $r = 120$

20. $s = 35 + (15/3)$

Ⓕ $s = 30$ Ⓖ $s = 35$ Ⓗ $s = 40$ Ⓚ $s = 45$

21. $376 \times 1{,}129 = 1{,}129 \times t$

Ⓐ $t = 0$ Ⓑ $t = 1$ Ⓒ $t = 376$ Ⓓ $t = 1{,}129$

22. $(927 \times 285) \times 103 = u \times (285 \times 103)$

Ⓕ $u = 927$ Ⓖ $u = 285$ Ⓗ $u = 103$ Ⓚ $u = 1$

Name Date

Solve each word problem.

23. Bob and Joan collect coins. Joan has 12 coins. Bob has 4 times as many coins as Joan. How many coins does Bob have?

Ⓐ 3 coins Ⓑ 16 coins Ⓒ 36 coins Ⓓ 48 coins

24. Vera and Tomas made sandwiches for a family picnic. Tomas made 27 sandwiches. That is 3 times as many as Vera made. How many sandwiches did Vera make?

Ⓕ 3 sandwiches Ⓖ 9 sandwiches Ⓗ 10 sandwiches Ⓚ 24 sandwiches

25. A toy store has stuffed bears, dogs, and cats on sale. They have 4 times as many stuffed bears as stuffed cats. They have one-half as many stuffed cats as stuffed dogs. Altogether the toy store has 28 stuffed animals on sale. How many of each kind of stuffed animal do they have?

Ⓐ 4 bears, 8 dogs, and 16 cats Ⓑ 8 bears, 16 dogs, and 4 cats

Ⓒ 16 bears, 4 dogs, and 4 cats Ⓓ 16 bears, 8 dogs, and 4 cats

Unit 1

Basic Multiplication and Division

What Is Assessed

- Recall basic multiplication and division.
- Identify and use the properties of multiplication and division.
- Solve one- and two-step problems involving multiplication.

Explaining the Assessment

1. Tell the students that they are going to investigate all the rectangular arrays they can make that will fit in a given area. They could draw a square with dimensions equal to 9 counters to model the classroom area available for desks.
2. Read the activity aloud with the class.

Materials

60 counters for each student, paper

Possible Responses

Question 1: Responses should include multiplication and division sentences for these arrays:

4 x 10 (4 x 10 = 40, 40 ÷ 10 = 4, 40 ÷ 4 = 10)

5 x 8	6 x 7	7 x 6	8 x 5	9 x 5
5 x 9	6 x 8	7 x 7	8 x 6	9 x 6
5 x 10	6 x 9	7 x 8	8 x 7	
	6 x 10			

Question 2: Groups may vary. Students may sort by width or length of array, or by size of product.

Question 3: 16 arrays

Question 4: Strategies may vary. Students may list all arrays with width of 4, then all arrays with width of 5, then 6, and so on.

Name ______________________ Date ______________________

ACTIVITY Making Arrays

You need to arrange 40 to 60 desks in a classroom. Nine desks fit across the classroom. 10 desks fit from front to back in the classroom. How many ways can you make a rectangular array of desks in this room?

1. On a sheet of paper, make all the arrays you can for multiplying two numbers with a product from 40 to 60. Remember, the columns and rows of desks cannot be longer or wider than the classroom.

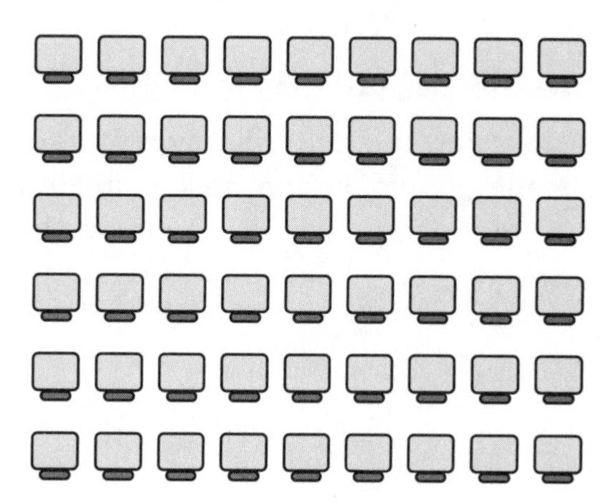

Write a multiplication sentence and a division sentence for each array. Then make the next array.

2. Sort your multiplication sentences for the arrays into groups.

3. How many arrays did you make? ______________________

4. Explain the strategy you used to find the greatest number of arrays.

____

____

____

Performance Assessment Rubric

An Exemplary Response (4 points)

- Systematically identifies all the arrays that will work for the problem
- Writes all related multiplication and division sentences correctly
- Clearly explains an organized strategy used to verify that all arrays have been found

A Proficient Response (3 points)

- Systematically identifies most of the arrays that will work for the problem
- Writes the related multiplication and division sentences correctly
- Explains a reasonable strategy used to verify that all arrays have been found

An Acceptable Response (2 points)

- Randomly finds more than half of the arrays that will work for the problem
- Does not select any arrays that are too big or too small for the problem
- Writes most related multiplication and division sentences correctly
- Explains why the arrays work for the problem

A Limited Response (1 point)

- Randomly finds some arrays that will work for the problem, and includes some that will not work
- Writes five or more related multiplication and division sentences incorrectly
- Does not explain a strategy for finding or verifying answers

Mini Unit A Test Form A Name ______________________ Date ______________

Find the perimeter and area of each figure.

1.

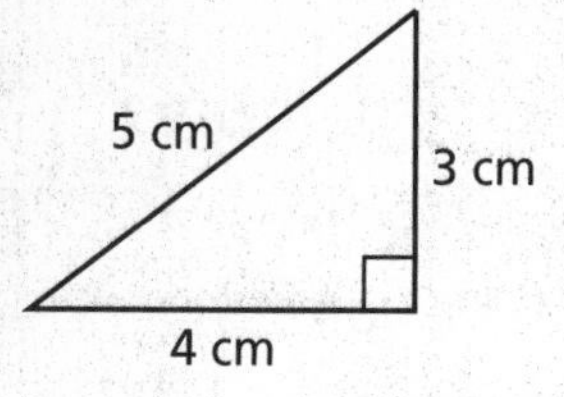

Perimeter 12 cm

Area 6 sq cm

2.

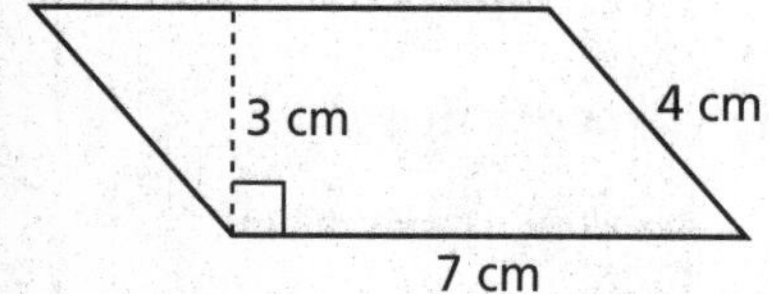

Perimeter 22 cm

Area 21 sq cm

3.

9 ft

3 ft 3 ft

9 ft

Perimeter 24 ft

Area 27 sq ft

4.

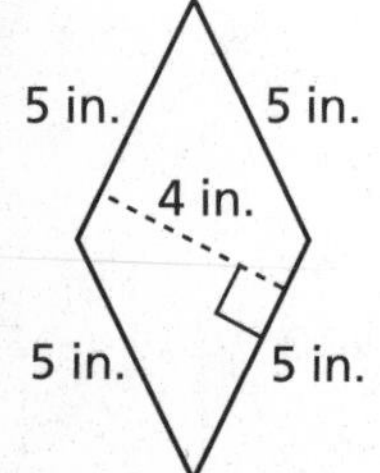

Perimeter 20 in.

Area 20 sq in.

Name _______________ Date _______________

The table in Mona's dining room is 6 feet long by 4 feet wide. Solve the problems about the table.

5. Mona wants to make a tablecloth to cover the whole top of the table. How many square feet of cloth does she need?

24 square feet

6. Mona wants to put a ribbon all the way around the edge of the table. How many feet of ribbon does she need?

20 feet

Find the perimeter and area of each figure.

7.

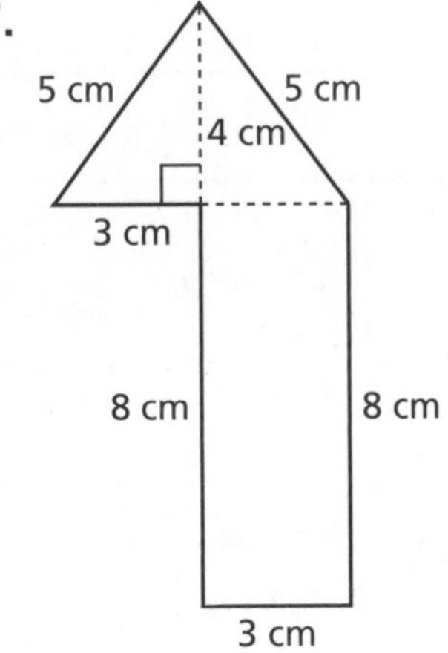

Perimeter 32 cm

Area 36 sq cm

8.

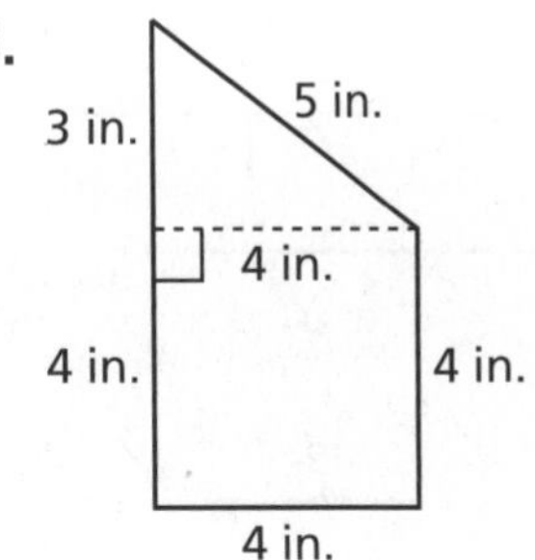

Perimeter 20 in.

Area 22 sq in.

Name Date

Solve the word problems.

9. A triangle has a base of 48 in. and a height of 3 ft. What is its area in square feet?

6 sq ft

10. **Extended Response** Brian is putting a fence around his garden. The garden is 4 feet wide and 7 feet long. He has 10 yd of fence. Does he have enough fence to put a fence all the way around his garden? Explain your answer.

Yes. The perimeter of the garden is 22 ft. Brian has 10 yd or 30 ft of fence. That is enough to go around the perimeter of the garden.

 Name **Date**

Fill in the circle for the correct answer.

Find the perimeter and area of each figure.

1.

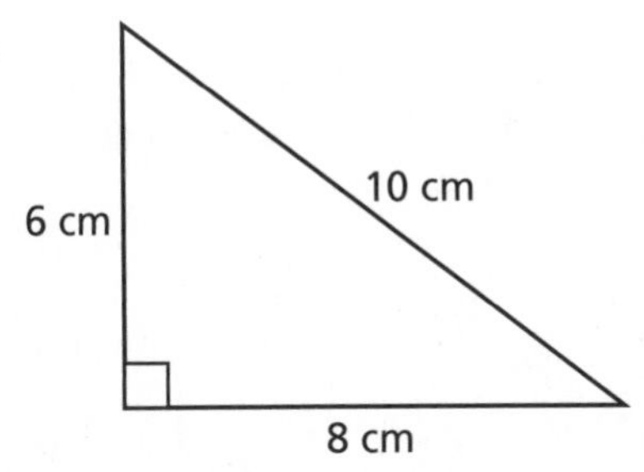

Ⓐ Perimeter = 14 cm; Area = 24 sq cm
Ⓑ Perimeter = 24 cm; Area = 24 sq cm
Ⓒ Perimeter = 24 cm; Area = 48 sq cm
Ⓓ Perimeter = 30 cm; Area = 48 sq cm

2.

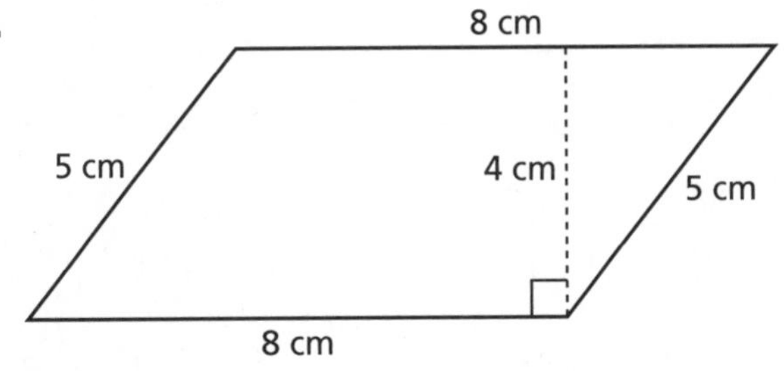

Ⓕ Perimeter = 26 cm; Area = 32 sq cm
Ⓖ Perimeter = 26 cm; Area = 40 sq cm
Ⓗ Perimeter = 32 cm; Area = 26 sq cm
Ⓚ Perimeter = 34 cm; Area = 32 sq cm

Name Date

3.

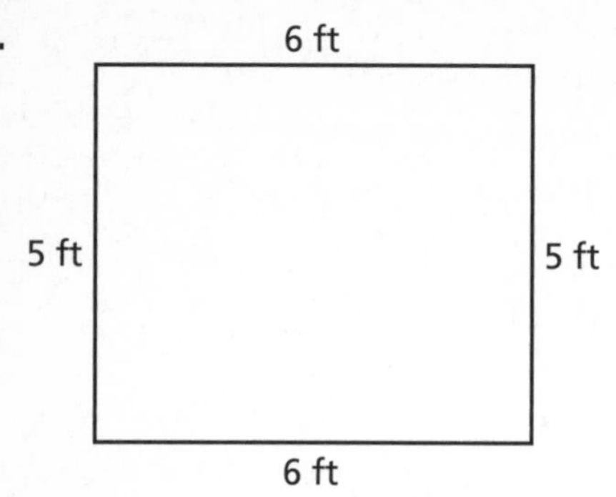

Ⓐ Perimeter = 11 ft; Area = 30 sq ft
Ⓑ Perimeter = 22 ft; Area = 15 sq ft
Ⓒ Perimeter = 22 ft; Area = 30 sq ft
Ⓓ Perimeter = 24 ft; Area = 36 sq ft

4.

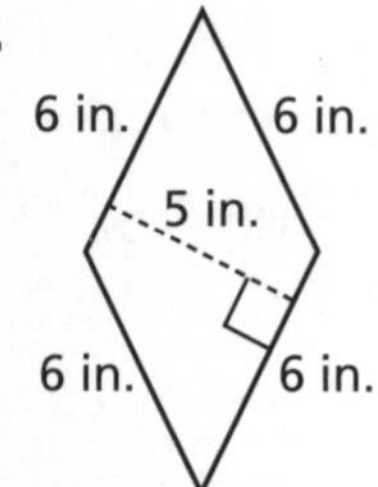

Ⓕ Perimeter = 11 in.; Area = 24 sq in.
Ⓖ Perimeter = 12 in.; Area = 25 sq in.
Ⓗ Perimeter = 18 in.; Area = 36 sq in.
Ⓚ Perimeter = 24 in.; Area = 30 sq in.

Name Date

The patio in Erika's back yard is 5 yards long by 4 yards wide. Solve the problems about the patio.

5. Erika's father wants to buy carpeting to cover the whole patio. How many square yards of carpeting does he need?

Ⓐ 16 square yards
Ⓑ 18 square yards
Ⓒ 20 square yards
Ⓓ 25 square yards

6. Erika's mother wants to put a fence all the way around the patio. How many yards of fence does she need?

Ⓕ 9 yards
Ⓖ 16 yards
Ⓗ 18 yards
Ⓚ 20 yards

Find the perimeter and area of the figure.

7.

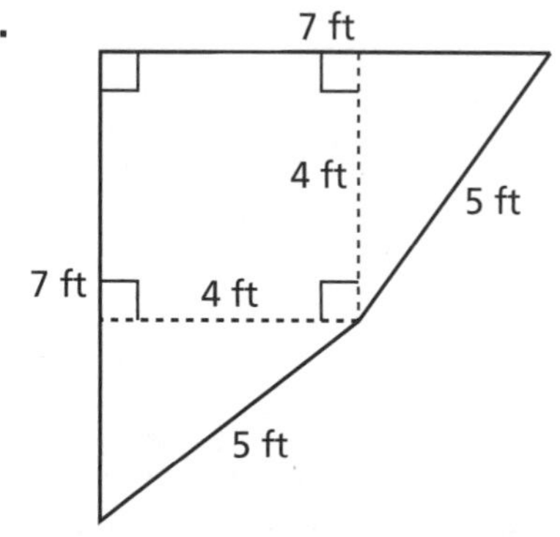

Ⓐ Perimeter = 24 ft; Area = 28 sq ft
Ⓑ Perimeter = 24 ft; Area = 40 sq ft
Ⓒ Perimeter = 28 ft; Area = 24 sq ft
Ⓓ Perimeter = 28 ft; Area = 28 sq ft

Name Date

Find the perimeter and area of the figure.

8.

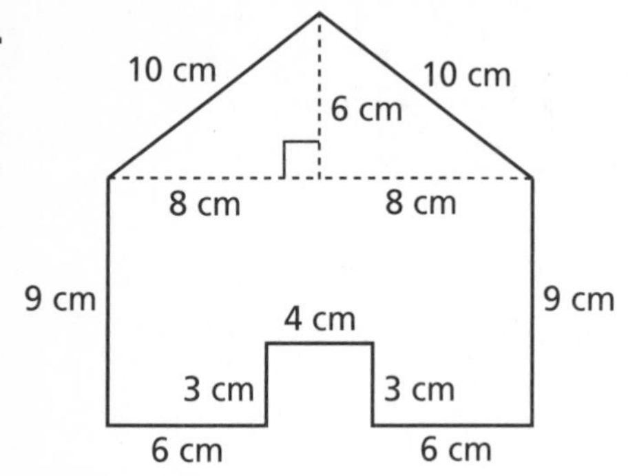

Ⓕ Perimeter = 54 cm; Area = 180 sq cm
Ⓖ Perimeter = 60 cm; Area = 180 sq cm
Ⓗ Perimeter = 60 cm; Area = 192 sq cm
Ⓚ Perimeter = 82 cm; Area = 180 sq cm

Solve the word problems.

9. A rectangle is 3 ft long and 24 in. wide. What is its area in square feet?
Ⓐ 5 sq ft
Ⓑ 6 sq ft
Ⓒ 10 sq ft
Ⓓ 72 sq ft

10. The tulip patch in a park is a rhombus. One side of the tulip patch is 6 ft long. The gardener at the park wants to put a fence all the way around the tulip patch. She has 7 yd of fence. How many more yards of fence does she need to be able to put a fence all the way around the tulip patch?
Ⓕ 1 yard
Ⓖ 2 yards
Ⓗ 3 yards
Ⓚ 4 yards

Mini Unit A

Perimeter and Area

What Is Assessed

- Find perimeter and area of polygons.
- Use metric measurements to solve problems involving perimeter and area.
- Find perimeter and area of complex figures.

Explaining the Assessment

1. Tell the students that they are going to make special figures called pentominos by attaching 5 squares together. All their pentominos must be different.

   Explain that these two pentominos are identical because you can flip one onto the other.

2. Read the activity aloud with the class.

Materials

Centimeter-grid paper

Possible Responses

Question 1:

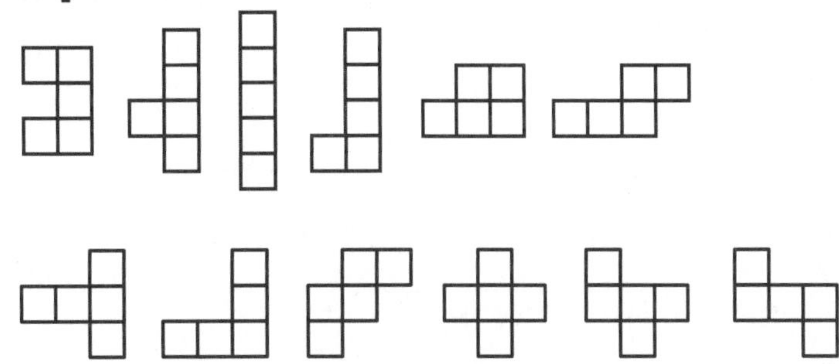

Question 2: There are 12 different pentominos.

Question 3: Every pentomino is made up of 5 squares. Each square is 1 sq cm in area. So every pentomino is 5 sq cm in area.

Question 4: All but one of pentominos have a perimeter of 12 cm. This one has a perimeter of 10 cm. It has more interior edges that are not part of the perimeter.

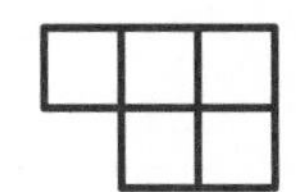

Name ______________________ Date ______________________

ACTIVITY Pentominos

A *pentomino* is a rectangle or complex figure made up of 5 attached squares.

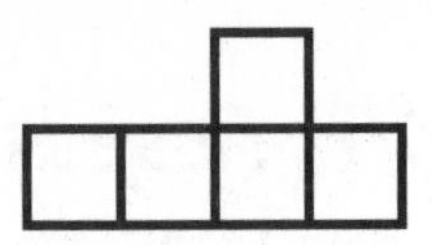

1. Draw as many different pentominos as you can on centimeter-grid paper.

   If you can flip or turn a pentomino to match another pentomino, then the two pentominos are not different.

2. How many different pentominos did you find?

   ____

3. Do all pentominos have the same area? Explain.

   ____
   ____
   ____
   ____

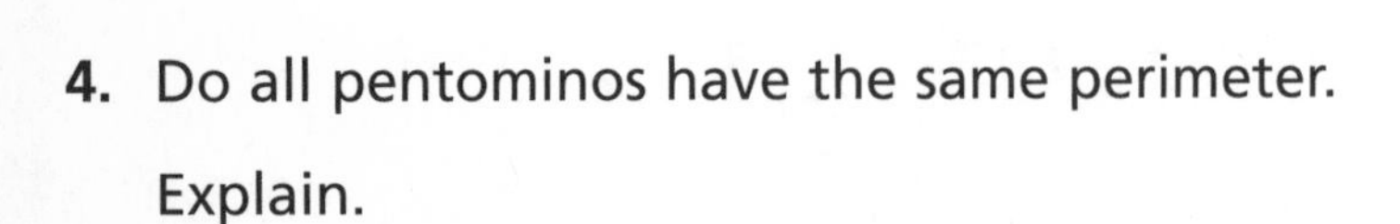

4. Do all pentominos have the same perimeter. Explain.

   ____
   ____
   ____
   ____

Performance Assessment Rubric

An Exemplary Response (4 points)

- Draws all 12 different pentominos
- Clearly explains why the areas are all the same
- Identifies the pentomino with a different perimeter and clearly explains why it is different

A Proficient Response (3 points)

- Draws at least 10 different pentominos with no duplicates
- Clearly explains why the areas are all the same
- May not draw the one pentomino with a different perimeter

An Acceptable Response (2 points)

- Draws at least 8 different pentominos; may have some duplicates
- Explains why the areas are all the same
- May not draw or identify the one pentomino with a different perimeter

A Limited Response (1 point)

- Draws fewer than 8 different pentominos; may have some duplicates
- May not be able to explain that the areas are the same, or explain why
- May not draw or identify the one pentomino with a different perimeter

Unit 2
Quick Quiz 1

Name ____________________ Date ____________

Write each number in standard form.

1. one billion, seven hundred twenty-six million, nine hundred fourteen thousand, seven hundred two 1,726,914,702

2. eight hundred forty-three thousandths 0.843

Write an equivalent decimal for each fraction.

3. $\frac{3}{10}$ 0.3

4. $\frac{52}{100}$ 0.52

Write these decimals in order from least to greatest.

5. 1.01 0.09 0.10 2.00 0.01

0.01 0.09 0.10 1.01 2.00

Unit 2
Quick Quiz 2

Name ____________________ Date __________

Add each pair of numbers.

1. 23,841 + 32,064 = 55,905

2. 384,071 + 205,178 = 589,249

Subtract each pair of numbers.

3. 50,000 − 23,901 = 26,099

4. 629,813 − 201,697 = 428,116

Compare. Write > (greater than) or < (less than).

5. 9,987,261 (<) 10,789,261

Unit 2
Quick Quiz 3

Name ______________________ Date ____________

Use the pictograph to answer each question.

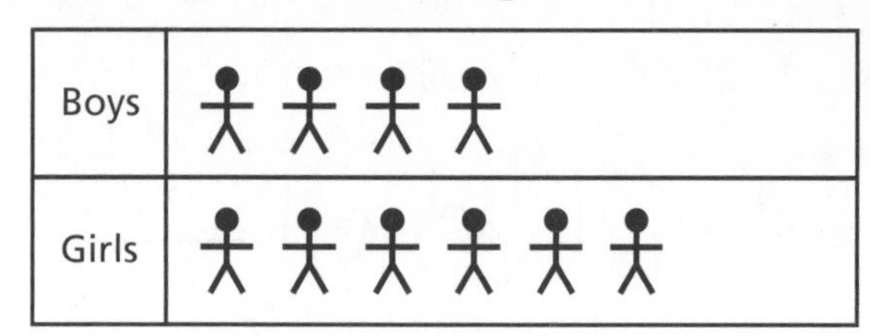

1. How many boys went to the soccer game? 40 boys

2. How many more girls than boys went to the soccer game? 20 more girls

Use the bar graph to answer each question.

Carnival Attendance

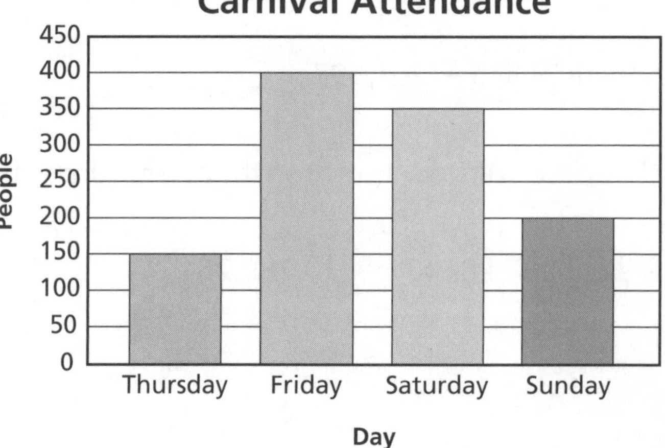

3. The graph shows the number of people who went to a carnival. To the nearest thousand, how many people went to the carnival? 1,000 people

4. How many more people went on Friday than went on Thursday? 250 people

Use the line graph to answer each question.

Sculpture Students

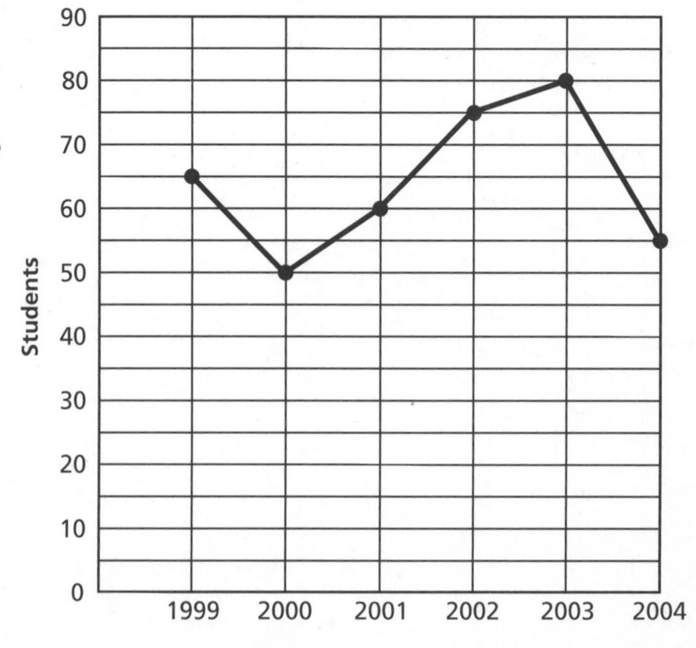

5. The graph shows the number of students who took sculpture class. How many students took sculpture class in 2000? 50 students

6. How many more students took sculpture class in 2003 than in 2000? 30 students

Unit 2 Quick Quiz 4	Name	Date

Write an equation for each problem, then solve.

Show your work.

1. A factory made 39,467 bolts in January. The factory made some more bolts in February. The factory made 62,011 bolts altogether in January and February. How many bolts did the factory make in February?

   $39,467 + b = 62,011$; 22,544 bolts

2. A school's students collected 50,000 cans to recycle. They took 32,579 of them to the recycling center. How many cans do they have left?

   $50,000 - 32,579 = c$; 17,421

3. There are 2,387 people seeing a movie. There are 5,896 more people seeing a play. How many people are seeing the play?

   $2,387 + 5,896 = p$; 8,283 people

Solve.

4. Rene earns $8.00 an hour mowing lawns. Last week she mowed lawns for 4 hours. She also earned $15.00 washing cars last week. How much did she earn last week?

   $47.00

5. Bill earns $7.50 per hour at his summer job. Last week he worked for 12 hours. Rene earns $6.75 per hour at her summer job. Last week she worked for 10 hours. How much more did Bill earn last week than Rene earned?

   $22.50

Unit 2 Test
Form A

Name ______________________ Date ______________

Write each number in standard form.

1. thirty-seven thousand, five hundred sixty 37,560

2. three million, six hundred two thousand, eight hundred twenty-four 3,602,824

3. seven tenths 0.7

4. five hundred twenty-eight thousandths 0.528

Compare. Write > (greater than) or < (less than).

5. 789,261 (<) 798,612

6. 3,491,652 (>) 3,419,652

7. 0.741 (>) 0.714

8. 0.08 (<) 0.6

Add each pair of numbers.

9. 652,721 + 201,054 = 853,775

10. 1.392 + 0.85 = 2.242

Subtract each pair of numbers.

11. 794,627 − 322,069 = 472,558

12. 6.418 − 1.37 = 5.048

Use the pictograph to answer each question.

13. How many birds are on the farm? 140 birds

14. How many more ducks than chickens are there on the farm? 40 more ducks

Use the bar graph to answer each question.

15. The graph shows the number of people at each basketball game last week. How many people saw a basketball game last week? 900 people

16. How many more people went to Game 2 than went to Game 1? 150 people

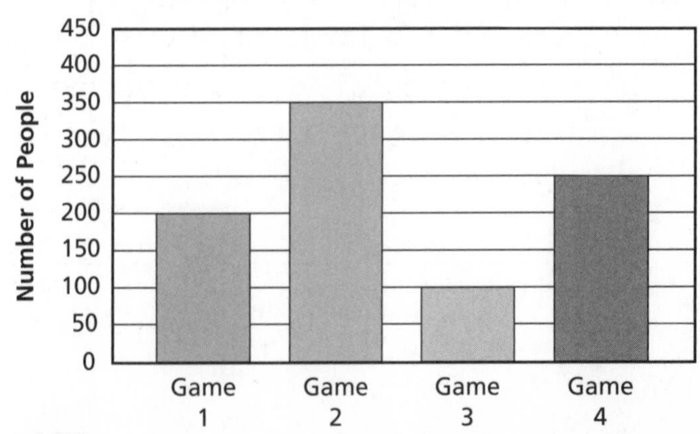

Name Date

Use the line graph to answer each question.

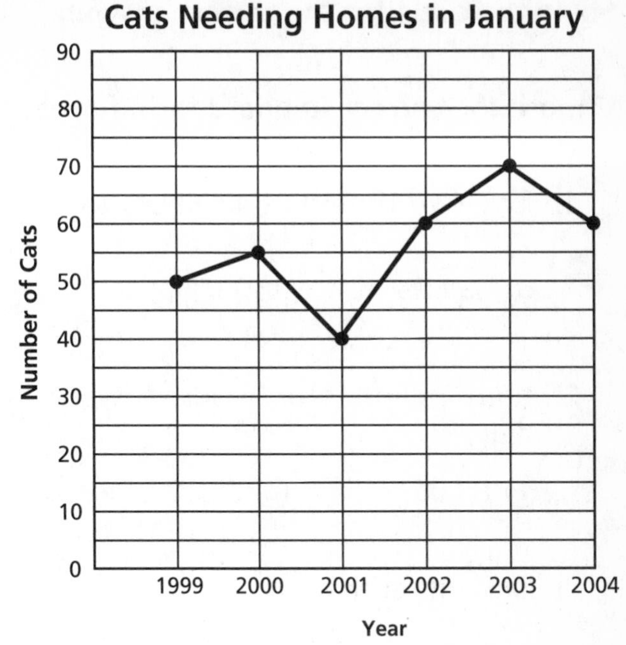

17. The graph shows the number of cats needing homes in January of six years. What was the number of cats needing homes in January 2004?

60 cats

18. How many more cats needed homes in 2003 than in 2004? 10 cats

Solve.

19. Nancy earns \$6.50 per hour at her summer job. Last week, she worked 15 hours. She bought a tennis racket for \$40 and put the rest in her savings account. How much did she put into her savings account?

$\$6.50 \times 15 = \$97.50$; $\$97.50 - \$40 = \$57.50$

Show your work.

20. **Extended Response** The distance between the library and the park is 1,563 feet. The distance between the library and the bank is 528 feet. The distance between the library and the fruit stand is 296 feet less than the distance between the library and the bank. Explain how to find how much greater the distance between the library and the park is than the distance between the library and the fruit stand.

First find the distance between the library and the fruit stand, $528 - 296 = 232$ feet. Then subtract the distance from 1,563, $1{,}563 - 232 = 1{,}331$. The distance between the library and park is 1,331 feet more than the distance between the library and the fruit stand.

Unit 2 Test
Form B

Name ____________________ Date ____________

Fill in the circle for the correct answer.

Choose the correct standard form for each number.

1. sixty-two thousand, five hundred nine

Ⓐ 26,509 Ⓑ 62,509 Ⓒ 62,590 Ⓓ 62,905

2. eight million, four hundred twenty thousand, six hundred thirty-seven

Ⓕ 8,000 Ⓖ 8,240 Ⓗ 8,240,637 Ⓚ 8,420,637

3. six hundredths

Ⓐ 0.06 Ⓑ 0.006 Ⓒ 0.0006 Ⓓ 0.00006

4. nine hundred forty-five thousandths

Ⓕ 0.0945 Ⓖ 0.459 Ⓗ 0.945 Ⓚ 945

Compare. What symbol makes each true?

5. 867,277 ◯ 876,722

Ⓐ > Ⓑ < Ⓒ =

6. 3,264,620 ◯ 3,624,620

Ⓕ > Ⓖ < Ⓗ =

7. 0.041 ◯ 0.140

Ⓐ > Ⓑ < Ⓒ =

8. 0.747 ◯ 0.724

Ⓕ > Ⓖ < Ⓗ =

Name ____________________ Date ____________________

Fill in the circle for the correct answer.

Add or subtract.

9. 238,721 + 401,566

Ⓐ 640,187 Ⓑ 640,287 Ⓒ 641,287 Ⓓ 740,287

10. 0.67 + 1.038

Ⓕ 1.708 Ⓖ 1.608 Ⓗ 0.708 Ⓚ 0.1708

11. 752,828 − 301,652

Ⓐ 454,176 Ⓑ 452,176 Ⓒ 451,176 Ⓓ 451,175

12. 6.872 − 1.53

Ⓕ 54.42 Ⓖ 53.42 Ⓗ 5.442 Ⓚ 5.342

Use the pictograph to answer each question.

13. How many students take painting class?

Ⓐ 120 students Ⓑ 130 students
Ⓒ 140 students Ⓓ 150 students

14. How many fewer girls than boys take painting class?

Ⓕ 20 fewer Ⓖ 30 fewer
Ⓗ 40 fewer Ⓚ 50 fewer

Students Taking Painting Class

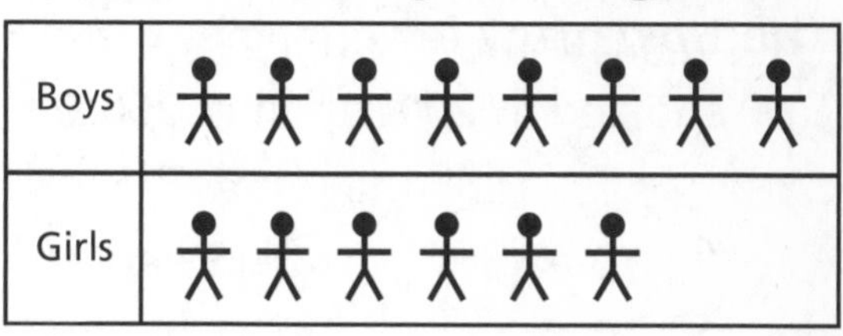

= 10 students

Name Date

Use the bar graph to answer each question.

15. The graph shows the number of apples sold at a fruit stand each day. How many apples were sold for the four days?

Ⓐ 800 apples Ⓑ 850 apples
Ⓒ 900 apples Ⓓ 950 apples

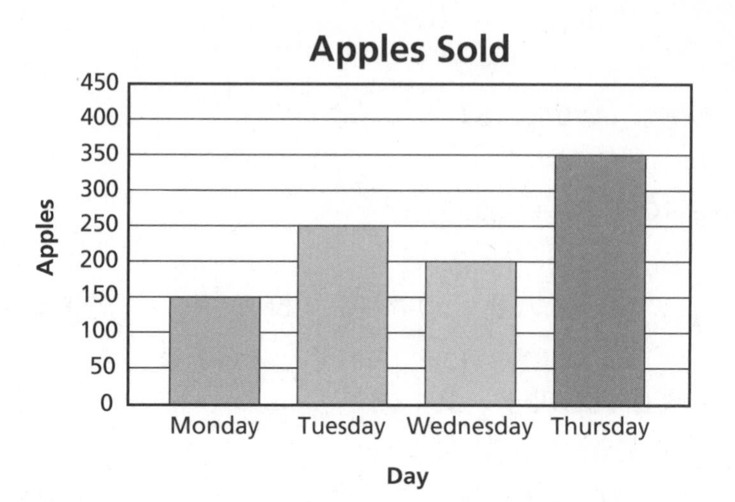

16. How many more apples were sold on Thursday than on Wednesday?

Ⓕ 150 apples Ⓖ 140 apples
Ⓗ 130 apples Ⓚ 120 apples

Use the line graph to answer each question.

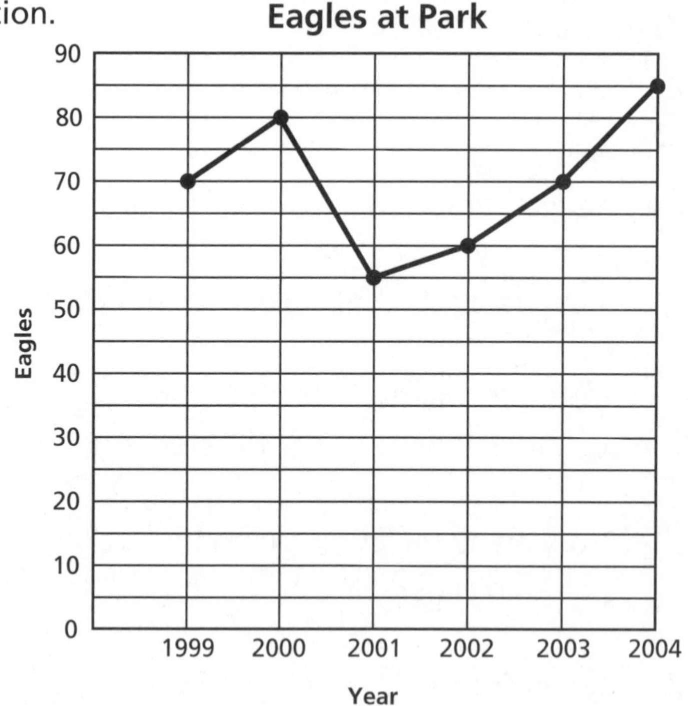

17. The graph shows the number of eagles spotted at a park each year. How many eagles were spotted in 2000?

Ⓐ 60 eagles Ⓑ 70 eagles
Ⓒ 80 eagles Ⓓ 90 eagles

18. How many fewer eagles were spotted in 2001 than in 2000?

Ⓕ 10 eagles Ⓖ 15 eagles
Ⓗ 20 eagles Ⓚ 25 eagles

Name Date

Solve.

19. Otto earns $6.50 per hour at his summer job. Last week, he worked for 14 hours. He bought a baseball bat for $55 and put the rest into his savings account. How much did he put into his savings account?

Ⓐ $14　　Ⓑ $36　　Ⓒ $55　　Ⓓ $91

20. A grocery store sold 1,852 potatoes. The store also sold 237 carrots. They sold 692 more onions than carrots. How many more potatoes did they sell than onions?

Ⓕ 23 more potatoes　　Ⓖ 237 more potatoes
Ⓗ 692 more potatoes　　Ⓚ 923 more potatoes

Addition and Subtraction With Whole Numbers and Decimals

What Is Assessed

- Read, write, and identify the place value of decimals and whole numbers.
- Add and subtract whole numbers and decimals.
- Solve a variety of problems involving addition and subtraction of whole numbers and decimals.

Explaining the Assessment

1. Tell the students that they will be creating a magic square in which all of the rows, columns, and diagonals have the same sum. Explain that they will need to test numbers to see if they work and then make changes to their work if necessary.
2. Read the activity aloud with the class.

Possible Responses

Question 1: 340

Question 2:

160	30	20	130
50	100	110	80
90	60	70	120
40	150	140	10

Question 3: Students should explain that to change the total 340 to 3.4 you need to divide by 100. Dividing by 100 changes 3 hundreds to 3 ones. If the total is divided by 100, then every addend must also be divided by 100.

1.6	0.3	0.2	1.3
0.5	1	1.1	0.8
0.9	0.6	0.7	1.2
0.4	1.5	1.4	0.1

Question 4: Students can use any number to add to, subtract from, or multiply or divide by to change every number in the square.

Name Date

ACTIVITY Magic Squares

This square is called "magic" because every row, column, and diagonal add up to the same number. That number is called the *magic sum*.

160	30	20	130
50		110	
	60	70	
			10

1. What is the magic sum for this magic square? ____________

2. Fill in the missing numbers in the magic square.

3. Show how you could use the first magic square to make a new one with a magic sum of 3.4. Explain why this will work.

____

____

____

____

4. Use one of the first two magic squares to make your own magic square with a different magic sum from the first two. Test your magic square. Explain how you created your square.

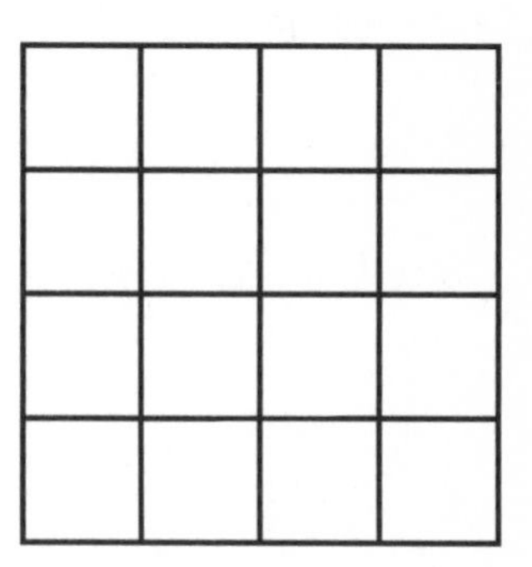

____

____

____

____

Performance Assessment Rubric

An Exemplary Response (4 points)

- Completes all puzzles without computational errors
- Using place-value concepts, explains why you can change the decimal point in each number and the square will still be magic
- Clearly explains the strategy used to create a new magic square; the strategy may contain complex operations or series of operations

A Proficient Response (3 points)

- Completes the first two puzzles without computational errors
- Explains that changing the magic sum means changing every number in the square the same way, such as dividing each number by 100
- Clearly explains the strategy used to create a new magic square

An Acceptable Response (2 points)

- Completes the first two puzzles with few computational errors
- Shows some understanding that changing the magic sum means changing every number in the square the same way
- Explains a simple strategy used to create a new magic square

A Limited Response (1 point)

- Completes the first puzzle with some computational errors
- Does not apply the concepts of multiplication or place value to create the second puzzle
- Does not create a new magic square that works

Name ______________________ Date ______________

Use these angles to answer questions 1 and 2.

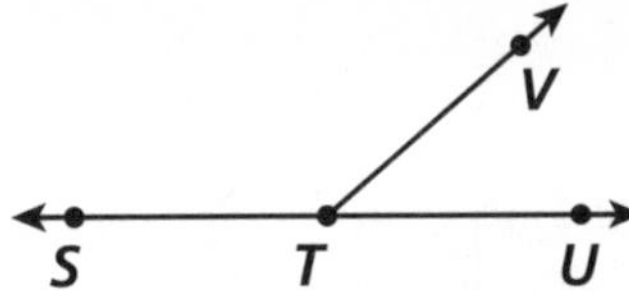

1. Name the pair of supplementary angles.

∠STV and ∠VTU

2. Name the straight angle.

∠STU

Write the measure of the unknown angle.

3.

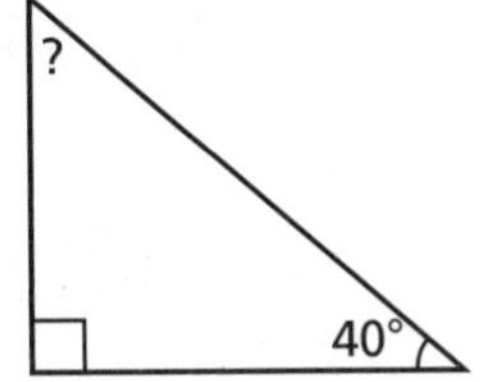

50°

4.

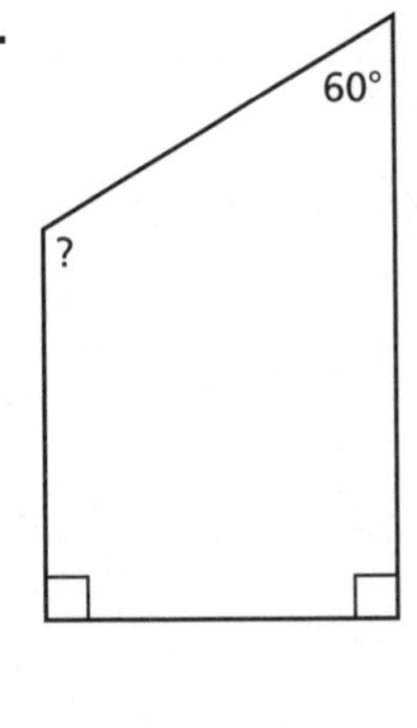

120°

5. Circle all the polygons that look congruent to each other.

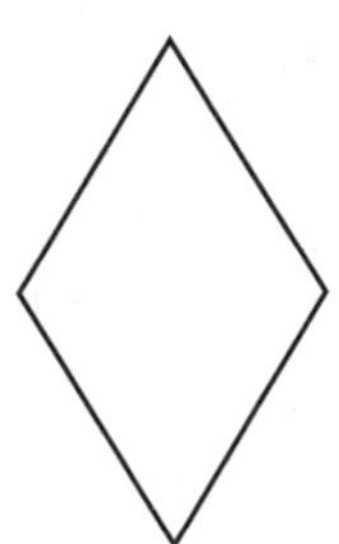
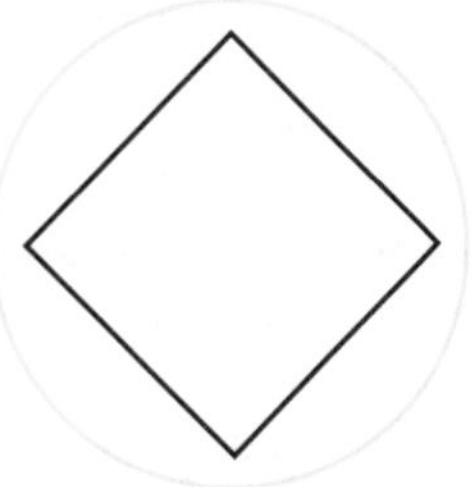
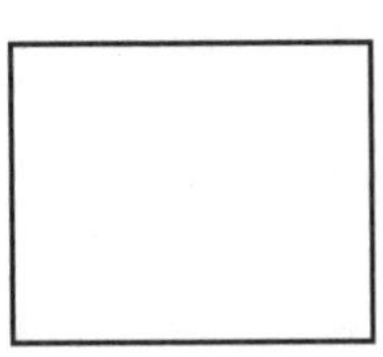
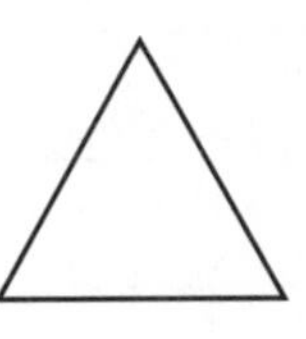

Name ____ Date _______________

6. Draw the figure after a counter-clockwise turn of 90°.

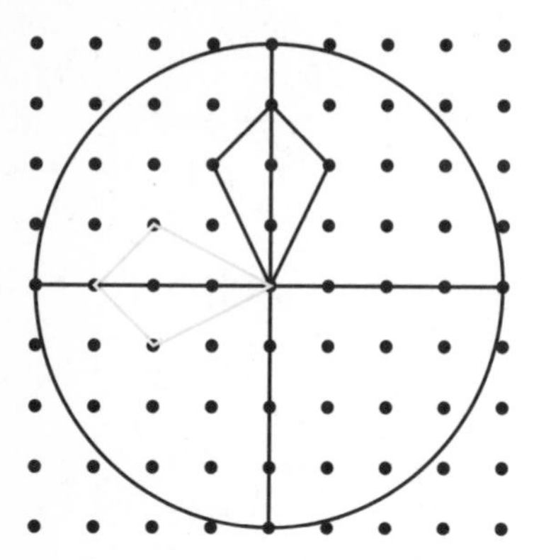

7. Draw all of the lines of symmetry for the hexagon.

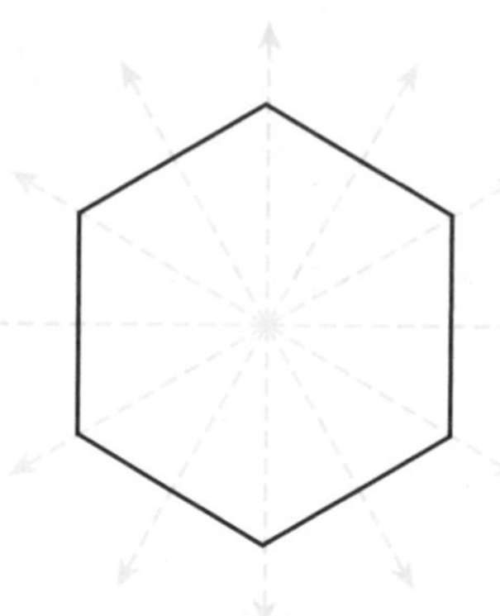

Use the circle graph to answer questions 8–10.

8. Which color did most people prefer?

Red

Yellow
Red
Blue

9. What color was preferred by the least number of people?

Yellow

10. **Extended Response** 153 people preferred red. 105 people preferred blue. How many people preferred yellow? Explain your answer.

48. It looks like the same amount of people preferred red as did yellow and blue combined. Because 105 + 48 = 153, 48 preferred yellow.

Fill in the circle for the correct answer.

Use these angles to answer questions 1 and 2.

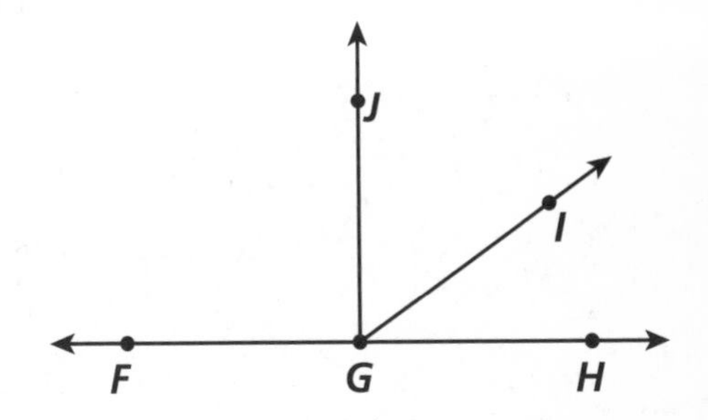

1. Which angle is straight?

Ⓐ ∠*FGH*

Ⓑ ∠*FGJ*

Ⓒ ∠*JGI*

Ⓓ ∠*JGH*

2. Which is a pair of complementary angles?

Ⓕ ∠*FGJ* and ∠*IGH*

Ⓖ ∠*FGJ* and ∠*JGH*

Ⓗ ∠*JGI* and ∠*IGH*

Ⓚ ∠*JGI* and ∠*JGH*

What is the measure of the unknown angle?

3.

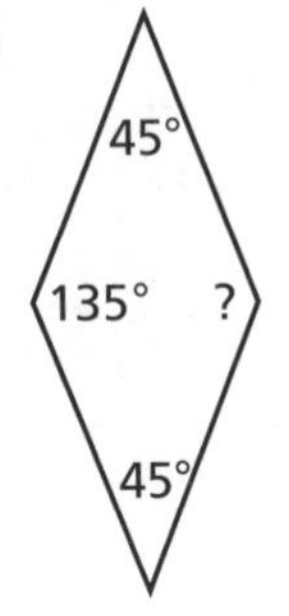

Ⓐ 45°

Ⓑ 135°

Ⓒ 180°

Ⓓ 360°

4.

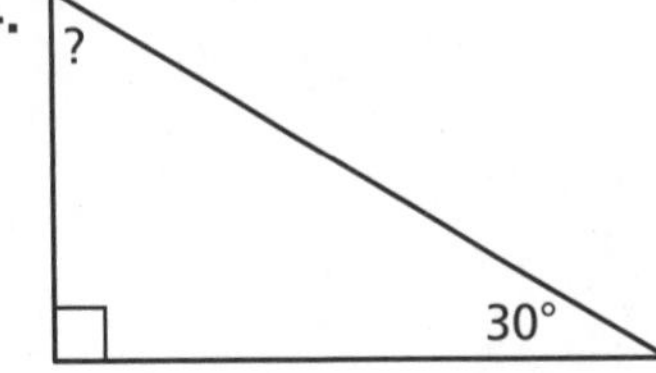

Ⓕ 180°

Ⓖ 150°

Ⓗ 90°

Ⓚ 60°

Which of these polygons are congruent?

5. Ⓐ A and B

Ⓑ C and D

Ⓒ B and E

Ⓓ A and E

A B C D E

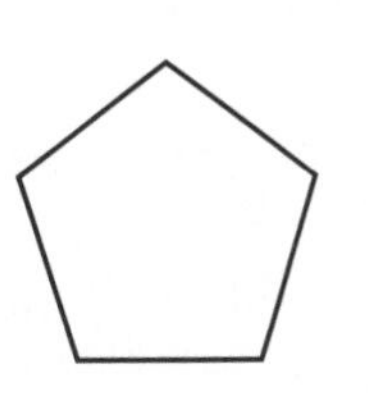

Name Date

Use this arrow to answer question 6. The arrow points right.

6. This arrow will point left after a
   Ⓕ 360° turn counter-clockwise.
   Ⓖ 180° turn clockwise.
   Ⓗ 90° turn clockwise.
   Ⓚ 90° turn counter-clockwise.

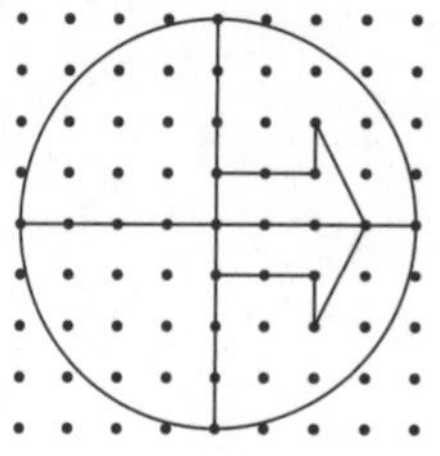

7. This figure has
   Ⓐ no lines of symmetry.
   Ⓑ one line of symmetry.
   Ⓒ two lines of symmetry.
   Ⓓ four lines of symmetry.

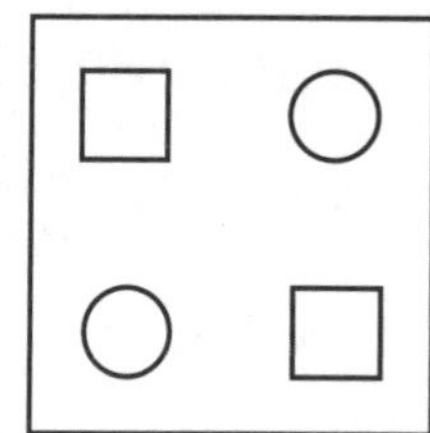

Use the circle graph to answer questions 8–10.

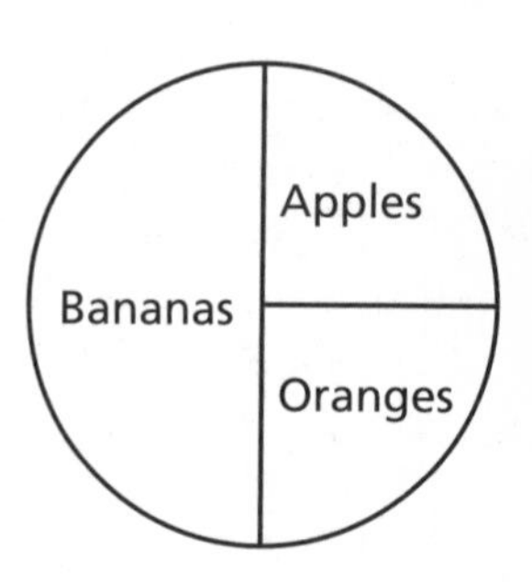

8. Which fruit did the most people say was their favorite?
   Ⓕ apples
   Ⓖ bananas
   Ⓗ grapes
   Ⓚ oranges

9. Which fruit was the favorite of the same amount of people as oranges?
   Ⓐ apples
   Ⓑ bananas
   Ⓒ grapes
   Ⓓ oranges

10. 15 people in the survey said they preferred apples. How many people were in the survey?
   Ⓕ 15 people
   Ⓖ 30 people
   Ⓗ 45 people
   Ⓚ 60 people

Circles, Polygons, and Angles

What Is Assessed

- Identify and measure angles.
- Identify congruent figures.
- Identify the position of an object after it has been turned.
- Identify lines of symmetry.

Materials

Protractor, centimeter-grid paper

Explaining the Assessment

1. To introduce the activity tasks, draw a circle on the board divided into six pieces. Explain that students will apply the knowledge they have gained in this unit to make conclusions about a large wheel of cheese that a store is cutting up in a similar manner.
2. Read the task aloud with the class.

Possible Responses

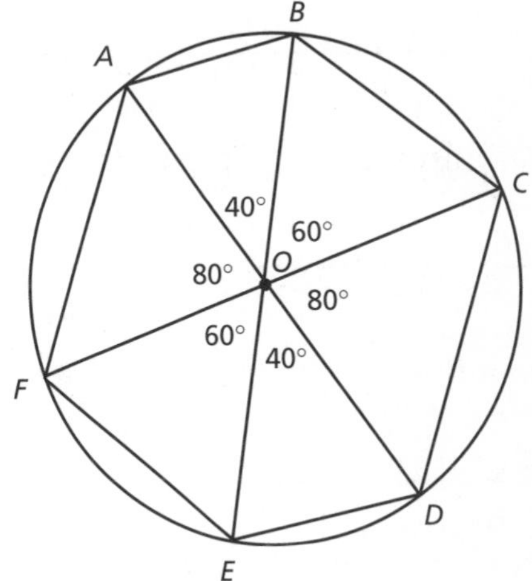

Question 1: 3 cuts

Question 2: a hexagon

Question 3: Triangles *AOB* and *EOD*
Triangles *AOF* and *COD*
Triangles *FOE* and *BOC*

These pairs of triangles have matching sides of equal length.

Question 4: Turn a triangle about *O* until it fits over the opposite triangle (or reflect the triangle in a diameter of the circle).

Question 5: lines *AD, FC,* or *BE*

Question 6: The total is 360°.

Question 7: The angles around the center form two straight angles on any of the lines of symmetry. So the total is 2 x 180° = 360°.

Name ______________________________ Date ______________

ACTIVITY The Big Cheese

Bob's Cheese Mart is dividing up a large, round piece of cheese into six pieces. Each cut of the cheese forms a diameter through the center.

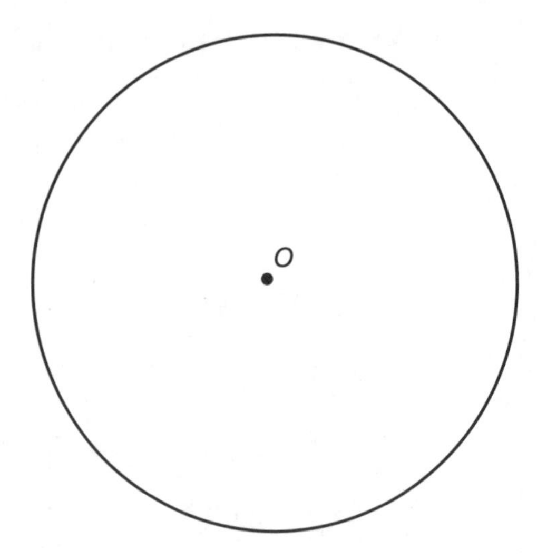

1. Draw diameters to divide Bob's cheese into 6 pieces. How many cuts did you have to make?

   ____

2. Label the six points on the edge of the cheese, *A, B, C, D, E,* and *F.* Join the points around the circle. What polygon did you make?

   ____

3. Name two congruent triangles. Why are they congruent?

   ______________________ ______________________

   ____

4. How could you transform one of the congruent triangles into the other?

   ____

5. Name a line of symmetry of the circle. ______________________

   ____

6. Measure and label the 6 angles at the center of the cheese. What is the total measure of the angles? ______________________

7. Explain how you could know the sum of the angles without adding.

   ____

   ____

Performance Assessment Rubric

An Exemplary Response (4 points)

- Identifies congruent triangles and clearly explains why the triangles are congruent
- Measures angles accurately (to nearest degree)
- Uses proper geometric reasoning efficiently to solve problems
- Describes a correct transformation
- Identifies a line of symmetry and the interior angle of a circle

A Proficient Response (3 points)

- Identifies and partially explains why triangles are congruent
- Measures angles accurately (to nearest 2 degrees)
- Uses geometric reasoning to solve problems
- Describes a correct transformation
- Identifies a line of symmetry and the interior angle of a circle

An Acceptable Response (2 points)

- Partially explains why triangles are congruent
- Measures angles within 10°
- May use incorrect reasoning to solve problems
- May describe an incorrect transformation
- May identify a line of symmetry and/or the interior angle of a circle

A Limited Response (1 point)

- May not identify congruent triangles or explain why triangles are congruent
- Measures angles inaccurately
- May use incorrect reasoning to solve problems
- May not describe a transformation
- May not identify a line of symmetry and/or the interior angle of a circle

Unit 3
Quick Quiz 1

Name ______________________ Date ____________

Add.

1. $\frac{3}{7} + \frac{2}{7} =$ $\frac{5}{7}$

2. $\frac{2}{3} - \frac{1}{3} =$ $\frac{1}{3}$

3. Write the mixed number as an improper fraction.

$3\frac{6}{11} =$ $\frac{39}{11}$

4. What fraction of the whole square is shaded?

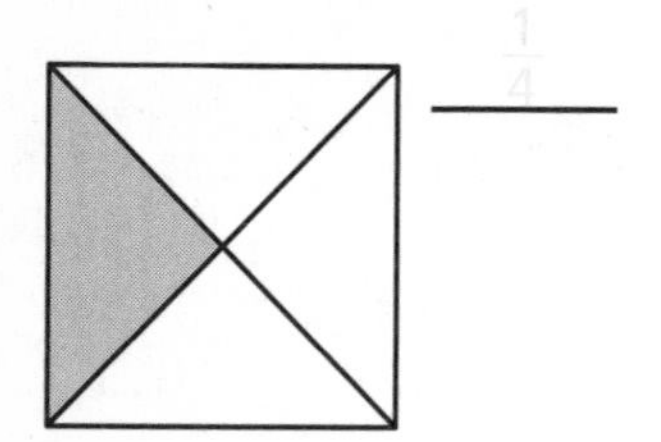

$\frac{1}{4}$

Fill in the correct fraction.

5. $\frac{3}{7} +$ $\frac{4}{7}$ $= 1$

Unit 3
Quick Quiz 2

Name ______________________ Date ____________

Write each mixed number as an improper fraction.

1. $4\frac{2}{3} =$ $\frac{14}{3}$

2. $5\frac{2}{7} =$ $\frac{37}{7}$

Add or subtract. Simplify your answers.

3. $5\frac{3}{4} + 3\frac{3}{4} =$ $9\frac{1}{2}$

4. $4\frac{5}{6} - 3\frac{1}{6} =$ $1\frac{2}{3}$

5. Write the fraction in inches and feet.

$5\frac{1}{3}$ feet = 5 feet 4 inches

Name ______________________ Date ____________

Add or subtract. Simplify your answers.

1. $3\frac{1}{6} + 4\frac{1}{3} =$ ________

2. $5\frac{5}{9} - 1\frac{1}{3} =$ ________

3. $6\frac{1}{4} - 5\frac{5}{12} =$ ________

4. Circle the equivalent fraction.

   $\frac{5}{9} =$ $\frac{15}{27}$ $\frac{12}{18}$ $\frac{20}{54}$

5. Jen rides the bus for $\frac{2}{3}$ of an hour before she gets off. Amy gets off the bus $\frac{1}{5}$ of an hour after Jen does. What is the total length of Amy's ride on the bus? ____________

Name ______________________________ Date ______________

Add or subtract. Simplify your answers.

1. $\frac{2}{5} + \frac{1}{5} =$ $\frac{3}{5}$

2. $\frac{5}{6} - \frac{1}{3} =$ $\frac{1}{2}$

3. $5\frac{3}{8} - 4\frac{5}{8}$ = $\frac{3}{4}$

4. $2\frac{1}{10} + 1\frac{1}{2}$ = $3\frac{3}{5}$

5. Circle the greater fraction. Then write > or < between the fractions. Explain your thinking.

$\frac{3}{8}$ (<) $\frac{3}{7}$

Sevenths are larger than eighths since it takes fewer of them to make a whole. Each fraction has a numerator of three, so three sevenths is greater.

6. Write the mixed number as an improper fraction. Show your work.

$3\frac{1}{3} = \frac{10}{3}$ $3\frac{1}{3} = 1 + 1 + 1 + \frac{1}{3} = \frac{3}{3} + \frac{3}{3} + \frac{3}{3} + \frac{1}{3} = \frac{10}{3}$

7. What fraction of the whole triangle is shaded?

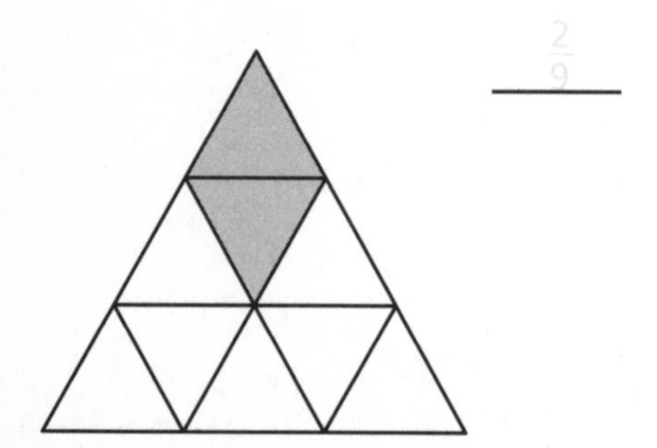

$\frac{2}{9}$

Name Date

8. Circle the fraction that is equivalent to $\frac{3}{5}$. Show your work.

$\frac{33}{50}$ $\frac{12}{20}$ $\frac{15}{35}$ $\frac{3}{5} \times \frac{4}{4} = \frac{12}{20}$

Solve. Simplify your answer.

9. Kellen has 5 red marbles and 10 yellow marbles in a bag. He reaches in and chooses 1 without looking. What is the probability that it is a red marble?

$\frac{1}{3}$

10. **Extended Response** Kim played in the park for $\frac{2}{3}$ hours. Later, Simone played for $\frac{1}{5}$ hours more than Kim. How many hours did they play altogether?

First calculate how long Simone played by adding both fractions together: $\frac{2}{3} + \frac{1}{5} = \frac{13}{15}$. Then add the amount of time that Kim played to the amount of time that Simone played: $\frac{13}{15} + \frac{2}{3} = 1\frac{8}{15}$. Together they played for $1\frac{8}{15}$ hours.

Name Date

Fill in the circle for the correct answer.

Add or subtract. Simplify your answers.

1. $\frac{2}{7} + \frac{3}{7} =$

Ⓐ $\frac{5}{14}$ Ⓑ $\frac{5}{7}$ Ⓒ $\frac{6}{7}$ Ⓓ $1\frac{3}{7}$

2. $\frac{4}{5} - \frac{3}{10} =$

Ⓕ $\frac{1}{15}$ Ⓖ $\frac{1}{10}$ Ⓗ $\frac{1}{2}$ Ⓚ $\frac{7}{10}$

3. $6\frac{1}{6} - 3\frac{1}{3}$

Ⓐ $2\frac{5}{6}$ Ⓑ 3 Ⓒ $3\frac{1}{9}$ Ⓓ $3\frac{1}{6}$

4. $3\frac{1}{4} + 1\frac{3}{8}$

Ⓕ $4\frac{1}{2}$ Ⓖ $4\frac{5}{8}$ Ⓗ 5 Ⓚ $5\frac{1}{8}$

5. Choose the greatest fraction.

Ⓐ $\frac{4}{9}$ Ⓑ $\frac{4}{10}$ Ⓒ $\frac{4}{11}$ Ⓓ $\frac{4}{12}$

Name Date

6. Choose the improper fraction that correctly completes the expression.

$2\frac{4}{5} =$

Ⓕ $\frac{12}{5}$ Ⓖ $\frac{14}{5}$ Ⓗ $\frac{14}{4}$ Ⓚ $\frac{24}{5}$

7. What fraction of the whole is shaded?

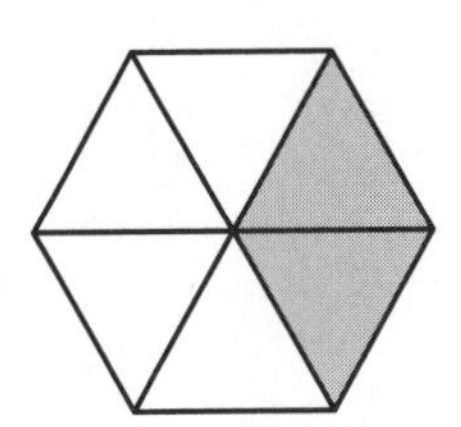

Ⓐ $\frac{1}{6}$ Ⓑ $\frac{1}{3}$ Ⓒ $\frac{2}{3}$ Ⓓ $\frac{5}{6}$

8. Which fraction is equivalent to $\frac{4}{7}$?

Ⓕ $\frac{8}{21}$ Ⓖ $\frac{20}{35}$ Ⓗ $\frac{8}{12}$ Ⓚ $\frac{7}{4}$

Solve.

9. Miami has 4 red pencils and 2 yellow pencils in her bag. She reaches in and chooses 1 without looking. What is the probability that it is a yellow pencil?

Ⓐ $\frac{1}{4}$ Ⓑ $\frac{1}{3}$ Ⓒ $\frac{1}{2}$ Ⓓ $\frac{2}{3}$

10. Peyton read for $\frac{3}{4}$ of an hour. Allison read for $\frac{4}{5}$ of an hour more than Peyton. How many hours did they read altogether?

Ⓕ $\frac{7}{9}$ Ⓖ $1\frac{3}{5}$ Ⓗ $2\frac{1}{5}$ Ⓚ $2\frac{3}{10}$

Unit 3

Fraction Concepts

What Is Assessed

- Add and subtract fractions with like and unlike denominators.
- Write and compare fractions.
- Find equivalent fractions.
- Solve problems involving fractions.

Explaining the Assessment

1. To introduce the activity tasks, talk with students about how fractions are used to show the results of surveys and make comparisons about the popularity of consumer items.
2. Read the activity aloud with the class.

Possible Responses

Question 1: Students need to find the sum of the 3 fractions and then find a fourth fraction that will make one whole.

$\frac{1}{6} + \frac{1}{3} + \frac{2}{5} = \frac{5}{30} + \frac{10}{30} + \frac{12}{30} = \frac{27}{30}$

$1 - \frac{27}{30} = \frac{3}{30} = \frac{1}{10}$

Question 2:

$\frac{1}{4} + \frac{1}{10} + \frac{3}{10} + \frac{3}{20} + \frac{1}{20} = \frac{17}{20}$

$1 - \frac{17}{20} = \frac{3}{20}$

Question 3: Answers will vary but they should show a sense of the order of popularity of the shirts. The fractions should also add to 1.

Name Date

ACTIVITY Sports Jersey Sales

Suppose your family has a store that sells sports jerseys. You need to decide on what types of jerseys to order for next year to stock the store shelves.

This table shows what customers say they may be looking to buy.

Type of jersey	baseball	basketball	hockey	soccer
Fraction	$\frac{2}{5}$	$\frac{1}{3}$		$\frac{1}{6}$

Color	white	red	green	blue	black	other
Fraction	$\frac{1}{4}$	$\frac{1}{10}$		$\frac{3}{10}$	$\frac{3}{20}$	$\frac{1}{20}$

1. What fraction of customers might buy a hockey jersey? Explain your answer.

____

____

2. What fraction of customers like green jerseys? Explain your answer.

____

____

3. Write 5 combinations of jerseys and colors, for example, white soccer jerseys. Decide what fraction of your store's order should be used for each type of jersey.

Jersey					
Fraction					

Explain how you decided on your fractions.

____

____

____

Performance Assessment Rubric

An Exemplary Response (4 points)

- Determines equivalent fractions and adds correctly
- Subtracts from 1 to find the missing fractions
- Chooses reasonable fractions for the shirt order and explains answers clearly
- Uses fractions that add to 1

A Proficient Response (3 points)

- Determines equivalent fractions and adds correctly
- Subtracts from 1 to find the missing fractions
- Chooses mostly reasonable fractions for the shirt order
- Uses fractions that add to 1

An Acceptable Response (2 points)

- Determines equivalent fractions but makes some errors in calculations
- Subtracts from 1 to find the missing fractions
- Chooses some reasonable fractions for the shirt order
- May not use fractions that add to 1

A Limited Response (1 point)

- Makes errors in calculations
- May not subtract from 1 to find the missing fractions
- Chooses unreasonable fractions for the shirt order
- May not use fractions that add to 1

Name ____________________ Date ____________

Find the volume of each prism.

1.

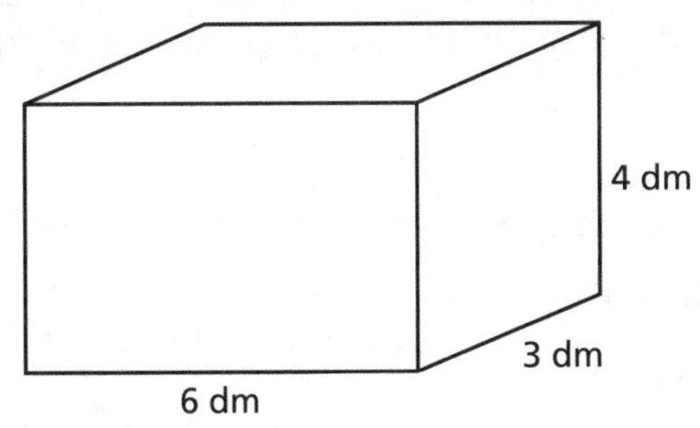

72 cu dm

2.

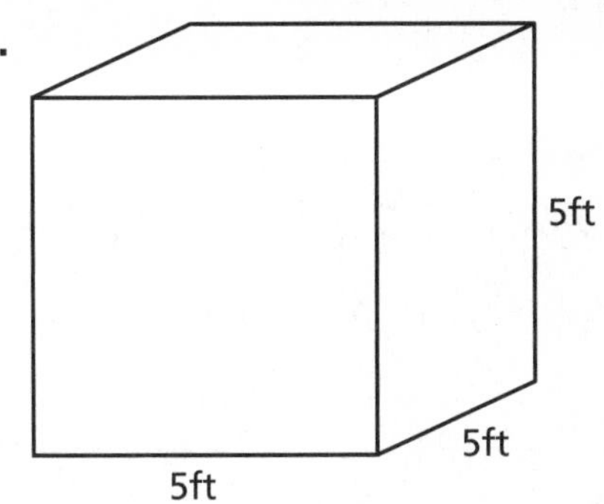

125 cu ft

3.

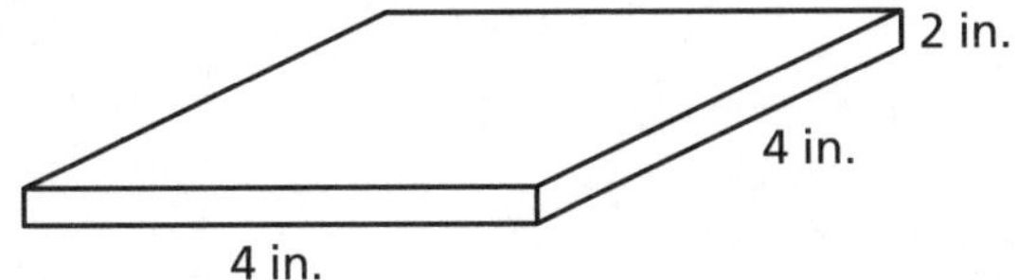

32 cu in.

4.

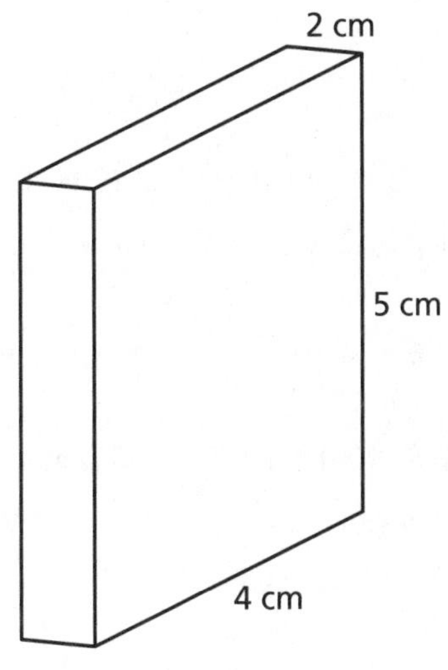

40 cu cm

Solve.

5. The lid of a box is 43 sq cm in area. The volume of the box is 430 cu cm. What is the height of the box?

10 cm

Name Date

6. Albert is making punch for a party. He combines 1,700 mL of soda with 600 mL of cherry juice. How many liters of punch will Albert make?

2.3 L

7. A recipe for a birthday cake requires $1\frac{1}{8}$ cups of sugar. Mary has $1\frac{1}{3}$ cups of sugar. Is that enough sugar to make the recipe?

Yes; $\frac{1}{8}$ is less than $\frac{1}{3}$

8. Ralph has 2 kg of carrots and 4 kg of chicken. He plans to use 1.3 kg of carrots and 1,500 g of chicken to make a stew. How many grams of each will not be used?

700 g of carrots and 2,500 g of chicken will not be used.

9. A washing machine is 3 ft wide, 3 ft deep, and 5 ft high. How much floor space will it cover?

It will cover 9 sq ft.

10. **Extended Response** One package weighs 68 ounces. Another package weighs $4\frac{1}{3}$ pounds. Which package is heavier? Explain your answer.

68 ounces is equivalent to 4 pounds 4 ounces. 4 ounces is less than $\frac{1}{3}$ of a pound so the package that weighs $4\frac{1}{3}$ pounds is heavier.

Name ______________________ Date ______________

Fill in the circle for the correct answer.

What is the volume of each prism?

1.

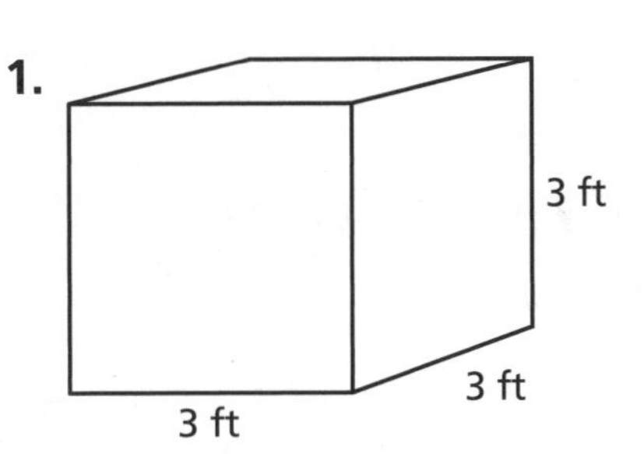

Ⓐ 1 cu ft
Ⓑ 9 cu ft
Ⓒ 18 cu ft
Ⓓ 27 cu ft

2.

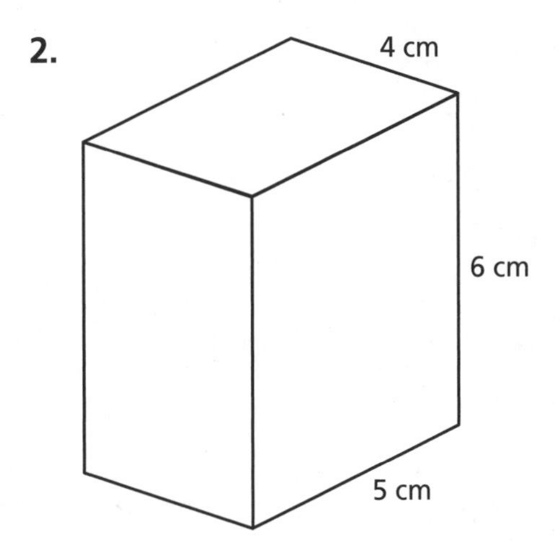

Ⓕ 120 cu cm
Ⓖ 115 cu cm
Ⓗ 20 cu cm
Ⓚ 15 cu cm

3.

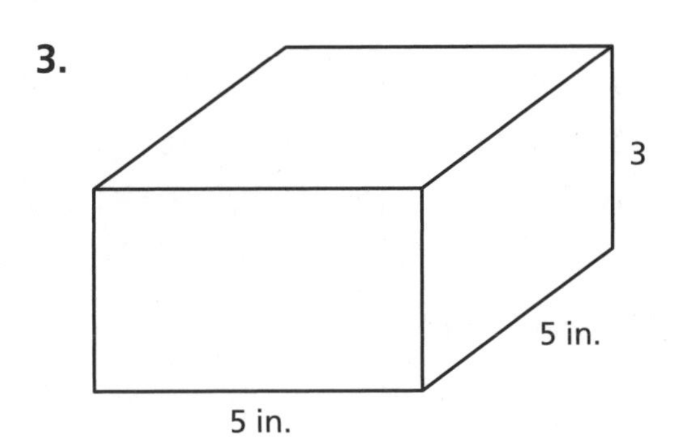

Ⓐ 11 cu in.
Ⓑ 18 cu in.
Ⓒ 60 cu in.
Ⓓ 75 cu in.

4.

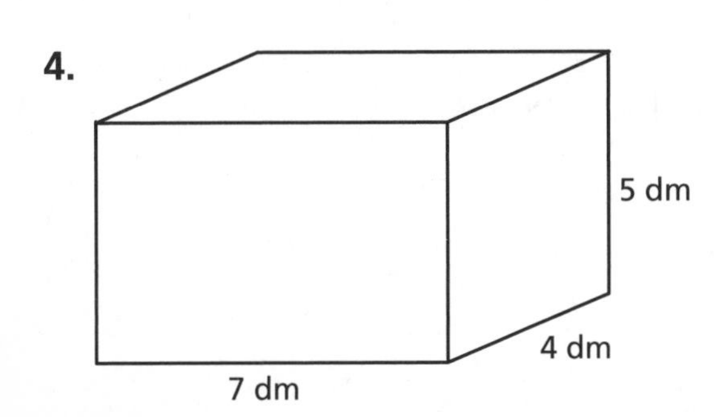

Ⓕ 70 cu dm
Ⓖ 140 cu dm
Ⓗ 250 cu dm
Ⓚ 275 cu dm

Name Date

Choose the answer that solves the equation.

5. The bottom of a trunk is 30 sq cm in area. The volume of the trunk is 510 cu cm. What is the height of the trunk?

Ⓐ 17 cm Ⓑ 170 cm Ⓒ 210 cm Ⓓ 480 cm

6. Wendy is making a bowl of mixed nuts. She has 1,200 g of peanuts and 900 g of cashews. How many kilograms of nuts will she have?

Ⓕ 1.9 kg Ⓖ 2.1 kg Ⓗ 21 kg Ⓚ 2,100 kg

7. Sandra is following a recipe to make chocolate chip cookies. The recipe calls for 24 ounces of chocolate chips. If Sandra wants just enough chocolate for the recipe but the grocery store only sells 4 sizes of bags, which size bag should she buy?

Ⓐ $\frac{1}{2}$ lb Ⓑ 1 lb Ⓒ $1\frac{1}{2}$ lb Ⓓ 2 lb

8. Quincy is making dinner. He has 4 kg of meat and 4 kg of onions. He plans to use 3.1 kg of meat and 800 g of onions. How many grams of each will not be used?

Ⓕ 100 g of meat and 3,000 g of onions Ⓖ 200 g of meat and 600 g of onions Ⓗ 900 g of meat and 3,200 g of onions Ⓚ 9,000 g of meat and 200 g of onions

9. A television is 4 ft wide, 3 ft deep, and 4 ft high. How much floor space will it cover?

Ⓐ 11 sq ft Ⓑ 12 sq ft Ⓒ 19 sq ft Ⓓ 48 sq ft

10. A box of books weighs 72 ounces. How many pounds does it weigh?

Ⓕ 4.5 Ⓖ 7.2 Ⓗ 6.3 Ⓚ 16.4

Volume, Capacity, and Weight

What Is Assessed

- Find the volume of a rectangular prism.
- Solve problems involving capacity, mass, and weight.

Explaining the Assessment

1. To introduce the activity tasks, tell students that Gilberto has a planter box and he wants to make a new one with twice the length, width, and height. He thinks doubling the dimensions will give him twice the amount of growing area and that he will need 80 cu dm of soil for the new box. Students will do calculations to show if they agree or disagree with Gilberto.
2. Review the formulas for area and volume.
3. Read the activity aloud with the class.

Possible Responses

Question 1: 4 dm by 10 dm by 8 dm

Question 2: area

Question 3: volume

Question 4: old box: 5 x 4 = 20 sq dm; new box 10 x 8 = 80 sq dm

Question 5: The growing area did not double. It quadrupled. Each dimension was doubled and area involves two dimensions. 2 x 2 = 4, so the area increases by 4 times.

Question 6: old box: 2 x 5 x 4 = 40 cu dm; new box: 4 x 10 x 8 = 320 cu dm

Question 7: No, Gilberto does not have enough soil. He has only 80 cu dm but he needs 320 cu dm.

Question 8: He wants to double each dimension and to find volume you use three dimensions. 2 x 2 x 2 = 8, so the volume increases by 8 times.

Name Date

ACTIVITY Building a Planter Box

Gilberto has a planter box with the length, width, and height shown.

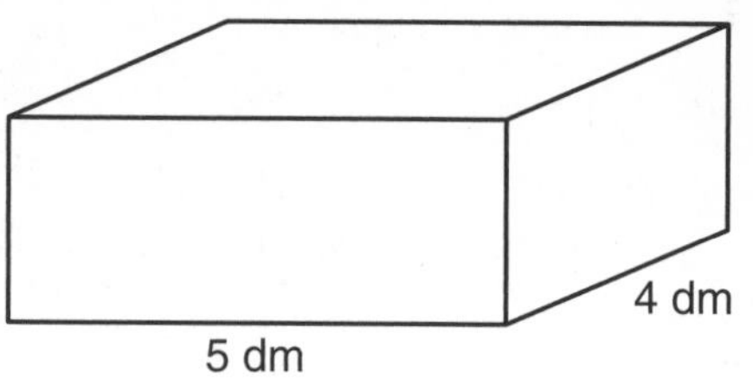

He wants to make a new one. He plans to double the length, width, and height. He has 80 cu dm of soil to put in it. He says the new box will have twice as much growing area and he will have enough soil to fill it. Do you agree or disagree?

1. What will the dimensions of the new planter box be? ______________________

2. To find the amount of growing area in each box, what do you need to find? Circle the correct measure.

   length width height area volume

3. To find the amount of soil for each box, what do you need to find? Circle the correct measure.

   length width height area volume

4. Calculate the growing area of each box. Include units in your answer.

   ____

   ____

5. Did the growing area double? Explain why or why not.

   ____

   ____

6. Calculate the volume of each box.

   ____

   ____

7. Does Gilberto have enough soil? ______________________

8. Explain why doubling each dimension does not result in twice the volume.

   ____

   ____

Performance Assessment Rubric

An Exemplary Response (4 points)

- Correctly identifies if a problem involves finding length, area, or volume
- Calculates area and volume with no errors and includes the correct units in the final answer
- Correctly observes that doubling dimensions does not result in twice the area or volume
- Uses mathematical language and calculations to efficiently show why doubling dimensions does not double area or volume

A Proficient Response (3 points)

- Correctly identifies if a problem involves finding length, area, or volume
- Calculates area and volume with no errors
- Correctly observes that doubling dimensions does not result in twice the area or volume
- Uses some mathematical language and calculations to show why doubling dimensions does not double area or volume

An Acceptable Response (2 points)

- Correctly identifies if a problem involves finding length, area, or volume
- Calculates area and volume with some calculation errors
- Correctly observes that doubling dimensions does not result in twice the area or volume
- Uses minimal mathematical language and calculations to show why doubling dimensions does not double area or volume

A Limited Response (1 point)

- Correctly identifies if a problem involves finding length, area, or volume
- Attempts to calculate area and volume but makes numerous calculation errors
- May observe that doubling dimensions does not result in twice the area or volume
- Does not explain why doubling dimensions does not result in twice the area or volume

Unit 4 Quick Quiz 1

Name ______________________ Date ______________

Solve. Use any method.

1. 34×71 = 2,414

2. 681×15 = 10,215

3. 58×302 = 17,516

4. 127×391 = 49,657

5. 72×19 = 1,368

6. 649×11 = 7,139

7. 69×182 = 12,558

8. 227×413 = 93,751

Unit 4 Quick Quiz 2

Name ______________________ Date ______________

Solve.

1. 100×0.46 = 46

2. 8.4×0.01 = 0.084

3. 3.67×10 = 36.7

4. 0.1×5.82 = 0.582

5. 3.2×0.7 = 2.24

6. 12.4×3.76 = 46.624

7. **Round the factors and multiply mentally to find the estimated answer. After finding the estimated answer, go back and find the exact answer.**

Estimated answer $0.31 \times 0.49 =$ 0.15

Exact answer $0.31 \times 0.49 =$ 0.1519

Unit 4
Quick Quiz 3

Name ______________________ Date __________

Solve.

1. $\begin{array}{r} 78 \\ 4\overline{)312} \end{array}$

2. $\begin{array}{r} 4,280 \\ 6\overline{)25,680} \end{array}$

3. $\begin{array}{r} 77.5 \\ 2\overline{)155} \end{array}$

4. $\begin{array}{r} 121.8 \\ 3\overline{)365.4} \end{array}$

5. $\begin{array}{r} 112.13 \\ 5\overline{)560.65} \end{array}$

6. $\begin{array}{r} 178.5 \\ 4\overline{)714} \end{array}$

Unit 4
Quick Quiz 4

Name ______________________ Date __________

Solve.

1. $\begin{array}{r} 57 \\ 0.1\overline{)5.7} \end{array}$

2. $\begin{array}{r} 624 \\ 0.5\overline{)312} \end{array}$

3. $\begin{array}{r} 135.6 \\ 0.5\overline{)67.8} \end{array}$

4. $\begin{array}{r} 500 \\ 0.07\overline{)35} \end{array}$

5. Juice glasses need to be filled. Each glass holds 0.2 liters. There are 4.5 liters of juice. How many glasses can be filled?

22 glasses

Unit 4 Test
Form A

Name ______________________ Date ______________

Solve.

1. $\begin{array}{r} 100 \\ \times\ 25 \\ \hline 2{,}500 \end{array}$

2. $\begin{array}{r} 7.3 \\ \times\ 0.01 \\ \hline 0.073 \end{array}$

3. $0.1\overline{)6.5}$ 65

4. $10\overline{)32.9}$ 3.29

Solve. Use any method.

5. $\begin{array}{r} 45 \\ \times\ 83 \\ \hline 3{,}735 \end{array}$

6. $\begin{array}{r} 277 \\ \times\ 23 \\ \hline 6{,}371 \end{array}$

7. $\begin{array}{r} 29 \\ \times\ 86 \\ \hline 2{,}494 \end{array}$

8. $\begin{array}{r} 340 \\ \times\ 534 \\ \hline 181{,}560 \end{array}$

Solve.

9. 0.042 × 85 = 3.57

10. 0.006 × 0.7 = 0.0042

11. Circle the two multiplications that have the same product.

7 × 0.5   (0.07 × 0.05)   0.07 × 0.5   (0.7 × 0.005)   0.07 × 5

12. Round the factors and multiply mentally to find the estimated answer. After finding the estimated answer, go back and find the exact answer.

Estimated Answer 0.92 × 0.47 = 0.45

Exact Answer 0.92 × 0.47 = 0.4324

Name Date

13. Round the divisor up or down to estimate the first number. Complete using any method you choose.

311 R12

$21\overline{)6{,}543}$

Divide.

14. $4\overline{)5{,}360}$ 1,340

15. $0.7\overline{)497}$ 710

16. $0.12\overline{)2.412}$ 20.1

17. Circle the division that does not have the same answer as the others.

63 ÷ 9 6.3 ÷ 0.9 0.63 ÷ 0.9 0.63 ÷ 0.09 0.063 ÷ 0.009

For each problem, decide whether you need to multiply or divide. Then solve.

Show your work.

18. A bag of peanuts contains 24.2 ounces. Five children want to share the peanuts equally. How many ounces of peanuts should each child get?

divide; 4.84 ounces

19. Strawberries cost $4.13 per pound. Jenna bought $12.39 worth of strawberries. How many pounds of strawberries did she buy?

divide; 3 pounds

20. **Extended Response** Explain how to divide 1,105 by 18 using estimation to determine the first digit of the quotient.

Answers will vary.

Unit 4 Test
Form B

Name ______________________ Date ______________

Fill in the circle for the correct answer.

Solve.

1. 100×45

Ⓐ 0.0045 Ⓑ 450
Ⓒ 4,500 Ⓓ 45,000

2. 6.7×0.01

Ⓕ 0.0067 Ⓖ 0.067
Ⓗ 0.67 Ⓚ K 67

3. $0.1\overline{)7.5}$

Ⓐ 0.0075 Ⓑ 0.075
Ⓒ 75 Ⓓ 750

4. $10\overline{)63.4}$

Ⓕ 0.634 Ⓖ 6.34
Ⓗ 63.4 Ⓚ 634

Solve. Use any method.

5. 35×76

Ⓐ 2,550 Ⓑ 2,560
Ⓒ 2,650 Ⓓ 2,660

6. 326×23

Ⓕ 6,498 Ⓖ 7,398
Ⓗ 7,488 Ⓚ 7,498

7. 23×75

Ⓐ 1,725 Ⓑ 1,735
Ⓒ 1,825 Ⓓ 2,725

8. 230×567

Ⓕ 130,310 Ⓖ 130,400
Ⓗ 130,410 Ⓚ 131,410

Solve.

9. 0.053×76

Ⓐ 0.4028 Ⓑ 4.028 Ⓒ 40.28 Ⓓ 402.8

Name Date

10. $0.007 \times 0.5 =$

Ⓕ 0.0035 Ⓖ 0.035 Ⓗ 0.35 Ⓚ 3.5

---

11. Which product is the same as 0.03×0.06?

Ⓐ 3×0.6 Ⓑ 0.03×0.6 Ⓒ 0.3×0.006 Ⓓ 0.03×6

---

12. Which is the best estimate for 0.49×0.68 when you round the factors to the nearest tenth?

Ⓕ 0.30 Ⓖ 0.32 Ⓗ 0.35 Ⓚ 0.45

---

13. Round the divisor up or down to estimate the first number. Complete using any method you choose.

$23\overline{)7{,}387}$

Ⓐ 320 R5 Ⓑ 321 R4 Ⓒ 321 R5 Ⓓ 322 R4

Name Date

Divide.

14. $4\overline{)5,608}$

Ⓕ 1,302 Ⓖ 1,402
Ⓗ 1,412 Ⓚ 1,502

15. $0.8\overline{)492}$

Ⓐ 6.15 Ⓑ 61.5
Ⓒ 615 Ⓓ 6.150

16. $0.13\overline{)4.251}$

Ⓕ 0.327 Ⓖ 3.27
Ⓗ 32.7 Ⓚ 327

---

17. Which is *not* the same as 42 ÷ 6?

Ⓐ 4.2 ÷ 0.6 Ⓑ 0.42 ÷ 0.6 Ⓒ 0.42 ÷ 0.06 Ⓓ 0.042 ÷ 0.006

Solve.

18. A bag of cherries contains 31.5 ounces. Six children want to share the cherries equally. How many ounces of cherries should each child get?

Ⓕ 0.525 ounces Ⓖ 5.25 ounces Ⓗ 52.5 ounces Ⓚ 525 ounces

19. Raisins cost $4.13 per pound. Jenna bought $16.52 worth of strawberries. How many pounds of strawberries did she buy?

Ⓐ 0.04 pounds Ⓑ 0.4 pounds Ⓒ 4 pounds Ⓓ 40 pounds

---

20. Use estimation to determine the first digit of 1,187 ÷ 47.

Ⓕ 1 Ⓖ 2 Ⓗ 3 Ⓚ 4

Unit 4

Multiplication and Division With Whole Numbers and Decimals

What Is Assessed

- Multiply and divide whole numbers using multiples of ten.
- Convert measurements into the same unit.
- Analyze data.
- Explain procedures and results.

Explaining the Assessment

1. Set the context for the task by telling students that animals can run at very different speeds. A speed always involves two units of measurement – distance and time. It tells you how far an animal can travel in a given amount of time.
2. Read the task aloud with the class.

Possible Responses

Question 1: The chicken runs 1,520 feet in 2 minutes. The squirrel runs 1,000 feet in 1 minute, so it can run 2 × 1,000 ft = 2,000 feet in 2 minutes. The squirrel is faster so it will get to the other side first.

Question 2:

Chicken: 1,520 ft ÷ 2 = 760 ft

Squirrel: 1,000 ft

Antelope: 60 miles in one hour ÷ 60 minutes = 1 mile in one minute

1 mile in one minute = 5,280 ft in one minute

Question 3:

The chicken travels 760 ft in a minute. The antelope travels 5,280 ft. 5,280 is about 7 times 760.

Some students may round numbers to 1,000 and estimate 5 times faster.

Some may round to 800 and 5,000 and estimate 6 times faster.

Some may use 7 × 8 = 56 and estimate 8 times faster.

Name _______________________________ Date _______________

ACTIVITY Running Times

A chicken can run 1,520 feet in 2 minutes.

An antelope can run 60 miles in one hour.

1. A squirrel can run 1,000 feet in 1 minute. If the chicken and the squirrel run across a road, which animal will be first to get to the other side? Explain.

____

____

____

____

2. How far can each animal run in one minute? Show your work

Chicken _______________________

Squirrel _______________________

Antelope _______________________

3. Estimate how many times faster an antelope is than a chicken. Check your estimate by multiplying.

____

____

____

Performance Assessment Rubric

An Exemplary Response (4 points)

- Always includes correct units of measurement
- Correctly converts speeds so that all show number of feet in one minute
- Checks and refines estimates until the best whole-number estimate is found

A Proficient Response (3 points)

- Always includes correct units of measurement
- Converts speeds correctly and compares them correctly
- Finds a reasonable estimate by rounding numbers and checking

An Acceptable Response (2 points)

- Shows all measurements and computations used to make comparisons; includes most units of measurement
- Compares at least 2 of the speeds correctly
- Makes a reasonable estimate, but doesn't show checking of results

A Limited Response (1 point)

- Some units may be converted incorrectly, or not included
- Some computations and comparisons may be incorrect
- Estimates may be unrealistic

Mini Unit D Test
Form A

Name ______________________________ Date ______________

Complete the image and name the transformation.

1.

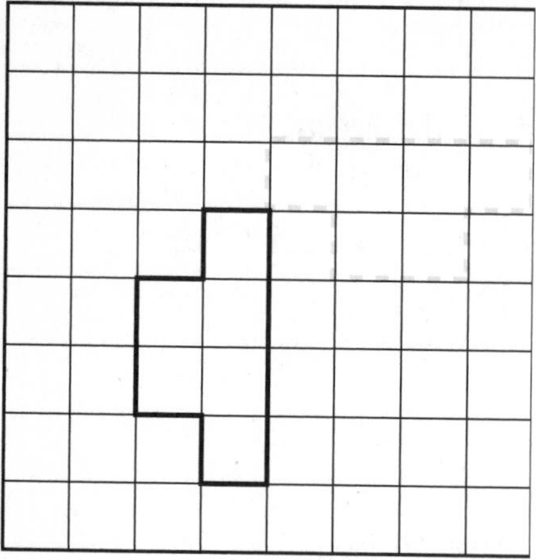

rotation

2.

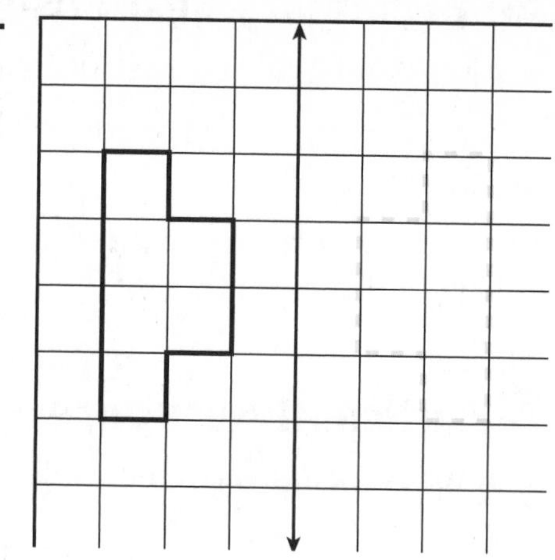

reflection

3.

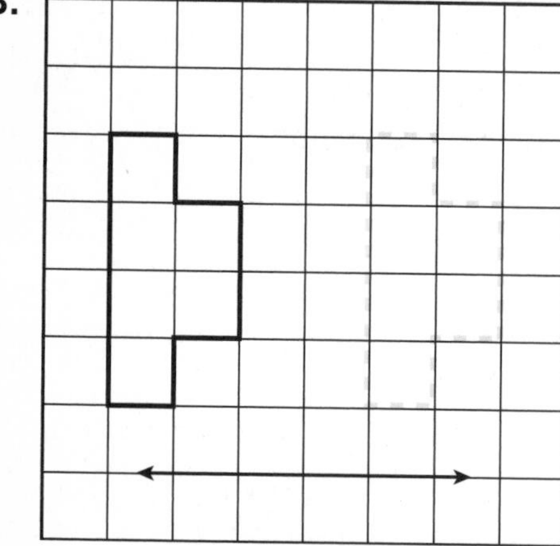

translation

Name ____________________ Date ____________________

4. Write an ordered pair for the location of point *A*.

(4, 7)

5. Draw and label point *B* at (6, 4).

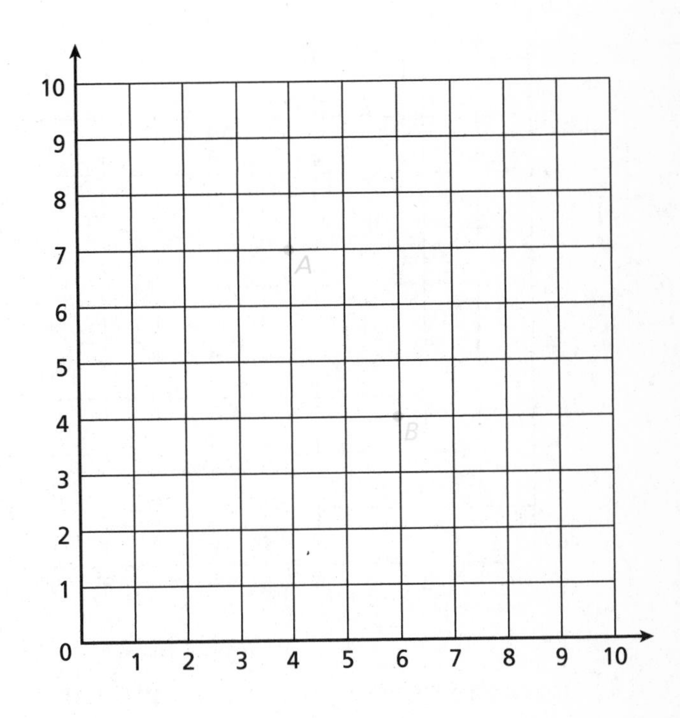

6. Write the words to describe the function $y = 3x$.

The value of y is 3 times the value of x.

7. Complete the table of ordered pairs.

$y = x + 3$	
x	y
1	4
2	5
3	6
4	7

8. Plot the ordered pairs from the table in exercise 7. Draw a line to connect the points.

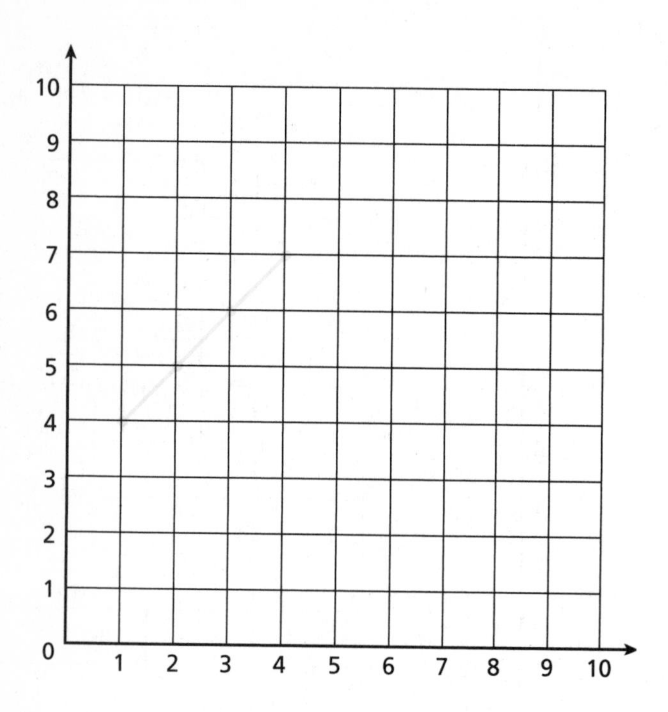

9. Draw the next figure in the pattern.

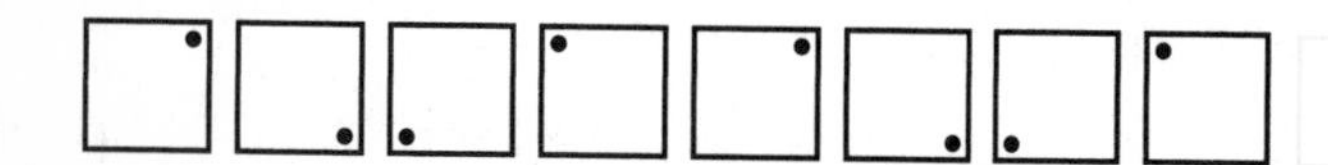

10. **Extended Response** Describe the pattern in exercise 9. Explain how to find the 16th figure in the pattern.

The corner that the circle is in makes a pattern: top-right, bottom-right, bottom-left, top-left. In the 5th figure the circle is in the top-right corner again and the pattern repeats. 16 is a multiple of 4, so I will see if the 16th figure is the same as the 4th figure. The circle is in the top-left corner in the 4th, 8th, 12th, and 16th figures. Therefore, the 16th figure is a square with a circle in the top-left corner.

Mini Unit D Test
Form B

Name ______________________ Date ____________

Fill in the circle for the correct answer.

Name the transformation.

1.

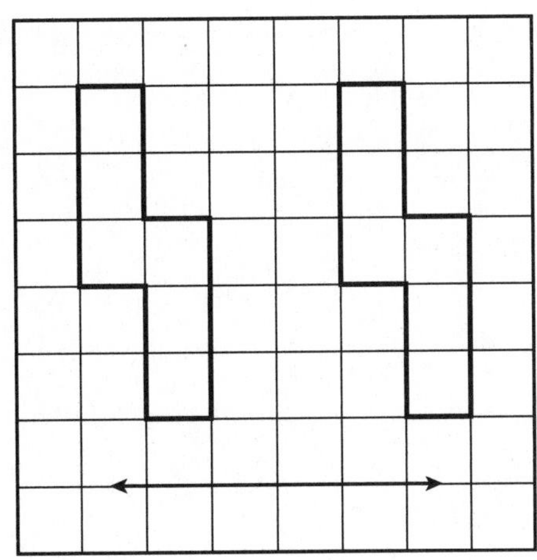

Ⓐ reflection
Ⓑ rotation
Ⓒ translation

2.

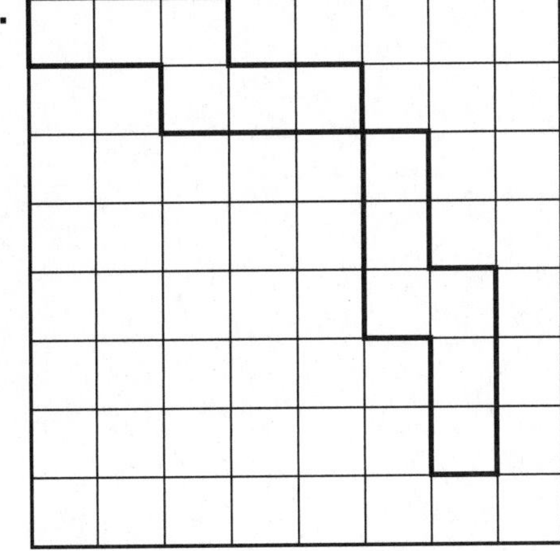

Ⓕ reflection
Ⓖ rotation
Ⓗ translation

3.

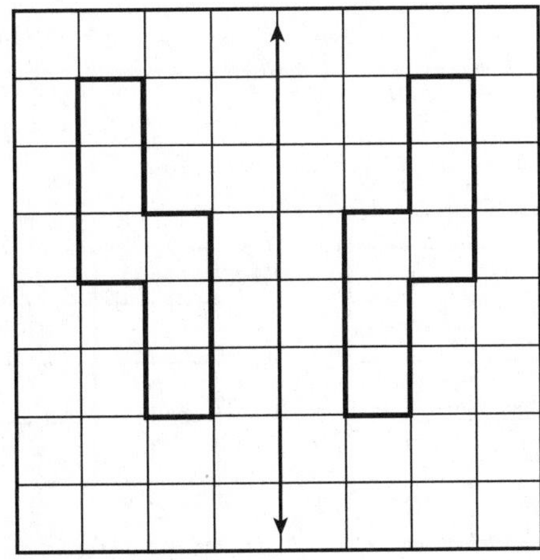

Ⓐ reflection
Ⓑ rotation
Ⓒ translation

Name Date

Use this graph to answer the questions.

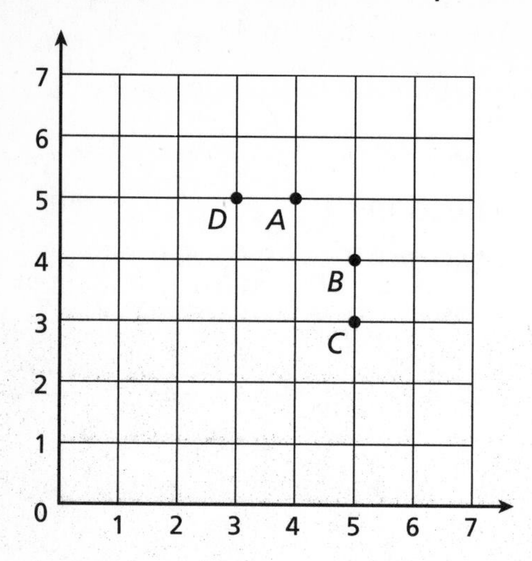

4. What is the ordered pair for the location of point *A*?

Ⓕ (5, 4) Ⓖ (5, 3) Ⓗ (4, 5) Ⓚ (3, 5)

5. Which point is at (3, 5)?

Ⓐ *A* Ⓑ *B* Ⓒ *C* Ⓓ *D*

6. Which words describe the function $y = 6x$?

Ⓕ The value of x is 6 more than the value of y.

Ⓖ The value of x is 6 times the value of y.

Ⓗ The value of y is 6 more than the value of x.

Ⓚ The value of y is 6 times the value of x.

---

7. Which table of ordered pairs shows the expression $y = x + 5$?

Ⓐ

x	y
1	3
2	4
3	5
4	6

Ⓑ

x	y
1	4
2	5
3	6
4	7

Ⓒ

x	y
1	5
2	6
3	7
4	8

Ⓓ

x	y
1	6
2	7
3	8
4	9

Name Date

8. Which line shows the ordered pairs from the correct table in exercise 7 with a line connecting them?

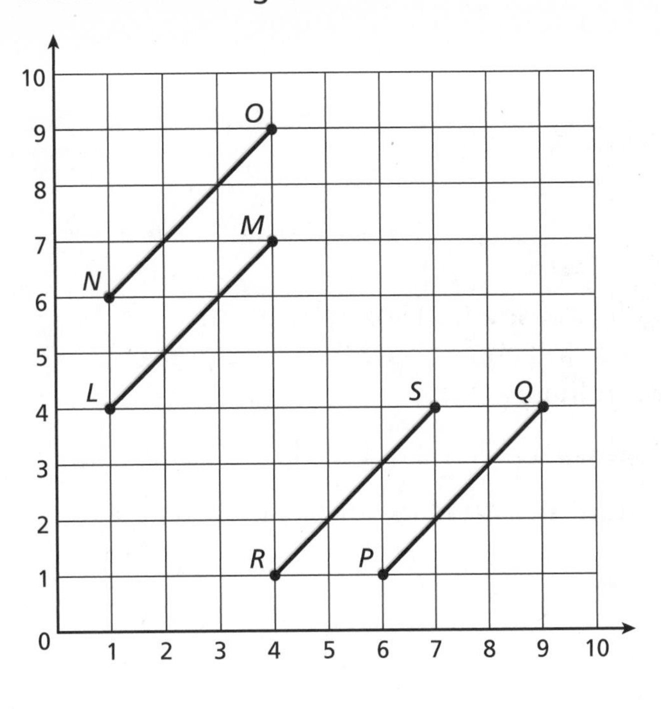

Ⓕ *LM* Ⓖ *NO* Ⓗ *PQ* Ⓚ *RS*

---

9. Choose the next figure in the pattern.

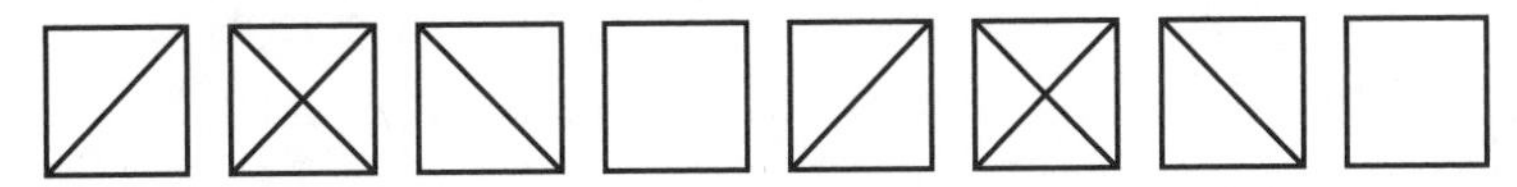

Ⓐ Ⓑ Ⓒ Ⓓ

10. What is the 16th figure in the pattern?

Ⓕ  Ⓖ  Ⓗ Ⓚ

The Coordinate Plane

What Is Assessed

- Recognize and complete rotations, reflections, and translations.
- Read and plot points on a coordinate grid.
- Identify patterns in motion geometry.

Explaining the Assessment

1. Tell the students that they will be making transformations of a triangle on a coordinate grid and finding out how the transformations change the coordinates.
2. Read the activity aloud with the class.
3. After completing Question 1, have the students cut out the triangle. As an option, they may glue the triangle on cardboard and use it to trace transformed triangles on the blank grid.

Possible Responses

Question 1: The coordinates are (1, 6), (1, 3), and (5, 3).

Question 2: The triangle may be flipped either horizontally or vertically and repositioned on the grid so that vertices are on grid points.

Question 3: The triangle may be rotated any multiple of 90° and repositioned on the grid so that vertices are on grid points.

Question 4: The triangle may be translated down by 1, 2, or 3 and left or right by 1 and repositioned on the grid so that vertices are on grid points.

Question 5: Every *x*-coordinate will increase by 1 if the triangle is translated 1 to the right, or decrease by 1 if it is translated 1 to the left. Every *y*-coordinate will decrease by the amount of the downward slide—1, 2, or 3.

Name Date

ACTIVITY Triangle Transformations

1. Write the coordinates of the vertices of the triangle.

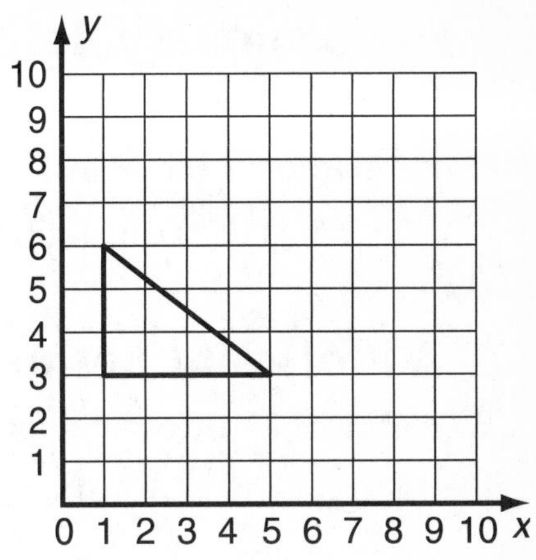

____

____

____

Cut out the triangle.

2. Flip the triangle and place it on the blank grid with its vertices on the grid. Write the new coordinates of its vertices here.

______________________ ______________________ ______________________

3. Rotate the triangle and place it on the blank grid with its vertices on the grid. Write the new coordinates of its vertices.

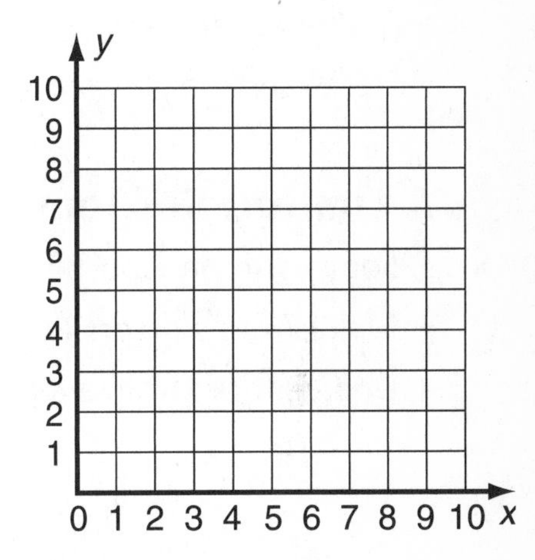

____

____

____

4. Translate the triangle to two different new positions on the grid. Write the new coordinates of the vertices for each.

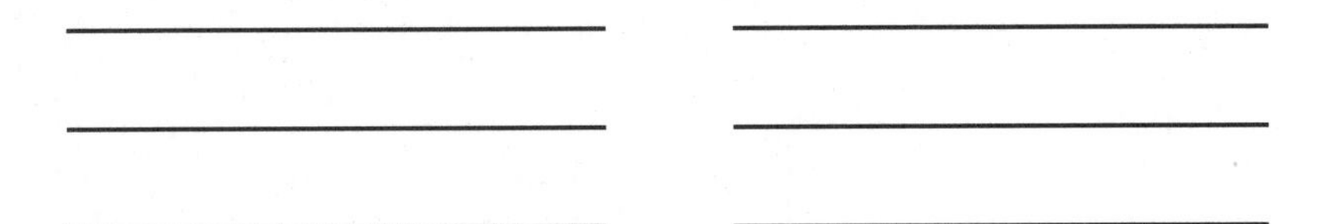

5. For each translated triangle, describe the pattern that changes the original coordinates to the new coordinates.

____

____

Performance Assessment Rubric

An Exemplary Response (4 points)

- Writes all the coordinates correctly
- Performs each transformation correctly
- Explains the translation patterns logically

A Proficient Response (3 points)

- Writes all original coordinates correctly
- Lists correct coordinates for most of the transformed vertices
- States correct rules for the translation patterns

An Acceptable Response (2 points)

- Writes all original coordinates correctly
- Makes several errors in transformed coordinates
- Describes the pattern for just one of the translated triangles

A Limited Response (1 point)

- Some original coordinates may be stated incorrectly
- Makes many errors in transformed coordinates
- Does not recognize a pattern in the translated coordinates

Unit 5 Quick Quiz 1	Name	Date

Multiply. Simplify your answers.

1. $8 \times \frac{1}{2} =$ ______ 4
2. $\frac{1}{8} \times 160 =$ ______ 20
3. $\frac{5}{6} \times 9 =$ ______ $\frac{45}{6} = \frac{15}{2}$
4. $\frac{3}{4} \times \frac{7}{12} =$ ______ $\frac{21}{48} = \frac{7}{16}$
5. $1\frac{1}{4} \times 1\frac{1}{5} =$ ______ $\frac{30}{20} = \frac{3}{2} = 1\frac{1}{2}$
6. $2\frac{2}{5} \times 7\frac{3}{8} =$ ______ $\frac{708}{40} = \frac{177}{10} = 17\frac{7}{10}$

Unit 5 Quick Quiz 2	Name	Date

1. Write the fraction and decimal equivalent for the shaded part of the circle.

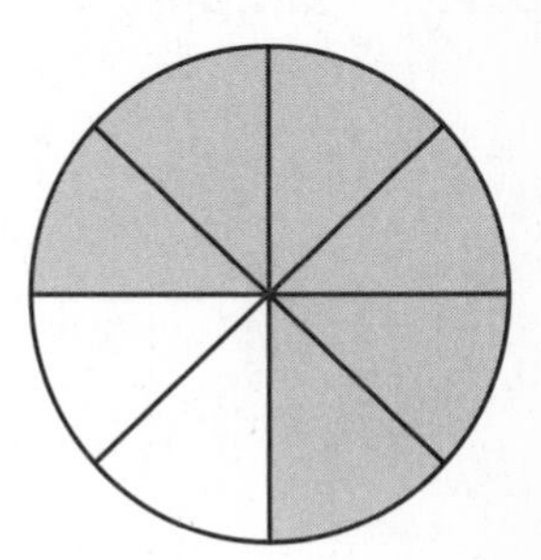

Fraction: ______ $\frac{6}{8} = \frac{3}{4}$

Decimal: ______ 0.75

2. Rewrite 0.35 as a fraction in simplest form. Show your work.

$0.35 =$ ______ $\frac{35}{100} = \frac{7}{20}$

Divide. Simplify your answers.

3. $15 \div \frac{1}{3} =$ ______ 45
4. $21 \div \frac{1}{7} =$ ______ 147

Solve. Name the operation to use. Simplify your answers.

5. Angela has a 12-meter long piece of ribbon. She is going to cut it into $\frac{1}{3}$-meter long pieces. How many pieces of ribbon will she have?

division; $12 \div \frac{1}{3} = 36$ pieces

Show your work.

Unit 5
Quick Quiz 3

Name ________________________ **Date** ____________

1. Rewrite $28 \times \frac{1}{4}$ as a division expression and show the answer.

$28 \div 4 = 7$

2. Rewrite $\frac{7}{8} \div \frac{1}{3}$ as a multiplication expression and show the answer.

$\frac{7}{8} \times 3 = \frac{21}{8} = 2\frac{5}{8}$

Divide. Simplify your answers.

3. $20 \div \frac{1}{5} =$ 100

4. $\frac{12}{3} \div \frac{6}{16} =$ $\frac{32}{3} = 10\frac{2}{3}$

5. $\frac{3}{8} \div \frac{2}{5} =$ $\frac{15}{16}$

Multiply. Simplify your answers.

1. $\frac{5}{6} \times 4 =$ $\frac{20}{6} = \frac{10}{3}$

2. $\frac{3}{4} \times \frac{7}{9} =$ $\frac{21}{36} = \frac{7}{12}$

3. Rewrite $15 \times \frac{1}{5}$ as a division expression and show the answer.

   $15 \div 5 = 3$

4. Rewrite $\frac{2}{3} \div \frac{1}{5}$ as a multiplication expression and show the answer.

   $\frac{2}{3} \times 5 = \frac{10}{3} = 3\frac{1}{3}$

5. Write the fraction and decimal equivalent for the shaded part of the circle.

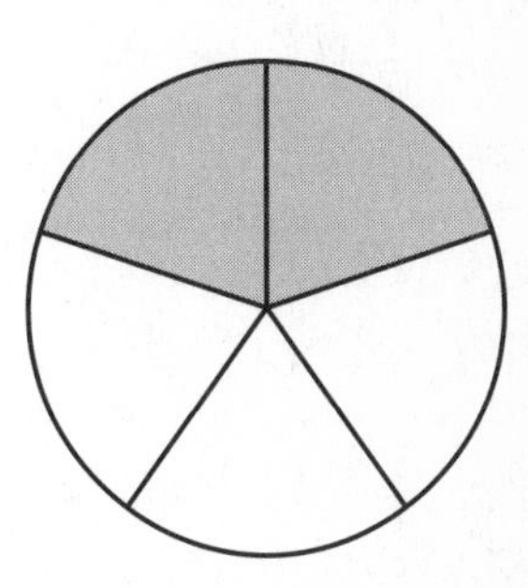

   Fraction: $\frac{2}{5}$

   Decimal: 0.4

6. Rewrite 0.25 as a fraction in simplest form. Show your work.

   $0.25 = \frac{25}{100} = \frac{1}{4}$

Divide. Simplify your answers.

7. $\frac{4}{5} \div 8 =$ $\frac{1}{10}$

8. $\frac{14}{15} \div \frac{2}{3} =$ $1\frac{2}{5}$

Name Date

Solve. Name the operation to use.
Simplify your answers.

Show your work.

9. Tracy walks $1\frac{4}{5}$ km 3 times each week. How many kilometers does she walk each week?

$\frac{9}{5} \times 3 = \frac{27}{5} = 5\frac{2}{5}$ km

10. **Extended Response** Terry and Lydia put 10 liters of water into their aquarium using a pitcher that can only hold $1\frac{1}{4}$ liters at a time. Lydia put in only the last pitcher of water. How many pitchers of water did Terry put in?

division; $10 \div \frac{5}{4} = 8$, Lydia put in the last pitcher of water, $8 - 1 = 7$ pitchers

Unit 5 Test Form B	Name	Date

Fill in the circle for the correct answer.

Multiply. Simplify your answers.

1. $\frac{5}{6} \times 15 =$

Ⓐ $\frac{5}{21}$ Ⓑ $\frac{75}{90}$

Ⓒ $\frac{20}{6}$ Ⓓ $\frac{25}{2}$

2. $\frac{4}{7} \times \frac{3}{8} =$

Ⓕ $\frac{3}{14}$ Ⓖ $\frac{7}{15}$

Ⓗ $\frac{12}{8}$ Ⓚ $\frac{12}{7}$

3. What is $15 \times \frac{1}{3} =$? written as a division equation?

Ⓐ $\frac{1}{5} \div \frac{1}{3} = \frac{1}{15}$ Ⓑ $\frac{1}{3} \div 15 = 5$ Ⓒ $15 \div 3 = 5$ Ⓓ $15 \div 5 = \frac{1}{3}$

4. What is $\frac{4}{5} \div \frac{1}{4} =$? written as a multiplication equation?

Ⓕ $\frac{4}{20} \times 4 = \frac{16}{3}$ Ⓖ $\frac{4}{5} \times \frac{1}{4} = \frac{16}{5}$ Ⓗ $\frac{4}{5} \times \frac{4}{4} = \frac{4}{20}$ Ⓚ $\frac{4}{5} \times 4 = \frac{16}{5}$

5. What is the decimal equivalent for the shaded part of the circle?

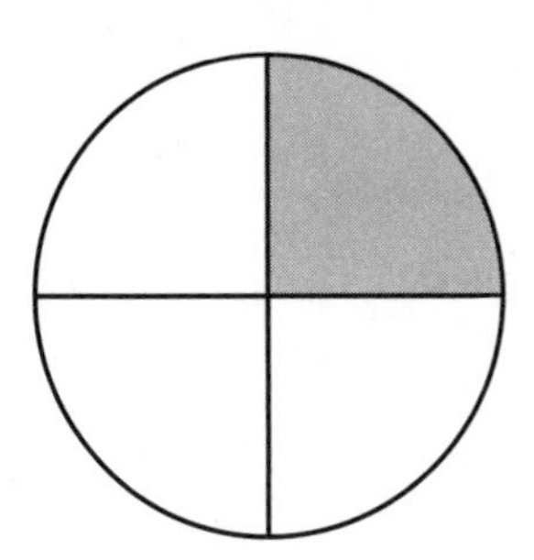

Ⓐ 0.25 Ⓑ 0.50 Ⓒ 0.75 Ⓓ 1.25

6. What is 0.45 as a fraction in simplest form?

Ⓕ $\frac{5}{100}$ Ⓖ $\frac{9}{20}$ Ⓗ $\frac{45}{100}$ Ⓚ $\frac{45}{10}$

Name Date

Divide. Simplify your answers.

7. $\frac{5}{7} \div 25 =$

Ⓐ $\frac{1}{35}$ Ⓑ $\frac{5}{175}$ Ⓒ $\frac{6}{32}$ Ⓓ $\frac{25}{7}$

8. $\frac{3}{4} \div \frac{9}{16} =$

Ⓕ $\frac{27}{64}$ Ⓖ $\frac{48}{36}$ Ⓗ $\frac{4}{3}$ Ⓚ $\frac{19}{13}$

Solve.

9. Paul rides his bike $1\frac{1}{10}$ mi every school day. How many miles does he ride in 5 school days?

Ⓐ 5 miles Ⓑ $5\frac{1}{2}$ miles Ⓒ $11\frac{1}{5}$ miles Ⓓ 55 miles

10. Ernest had a piece of yarn 30 m long. He cut the yarn into $1\frac{1}{4}$ m pieces. Ernest's sister has 3 more pieces of yarn than he does. How many pieces of yarn does Ernest's sister have?

Ⓕ 21 pieces Ⓖ 24 pieces Ⓗ 27 pieces Ⓚ 33 pieces

Unit 5

Multiplication and Division With Fractions

What Is Assessed

- Multiply fractions and mixed numbers.
- Relate fractional operations.
- Divide fractions and mixed numbers.

Explaining the Assessment

1. Tell the students that they will be making multiplication and division equations with fractions. First they will finish partially-completed equations.
2. Read the activity aloud with the class.
3. After completing Question 1, ask the students if they can simplify the answer.
4. Prompt them to use logic and a Guess and Check strategy to find the missing numbers in exercise 3. For a product of $\frac{2}{5}$, the denominator of one factor has to be 5.

Possible Responses

Question 1: The product $\frac{9}{24}$ simplifies to $\frac{3}{8}$. Some students may write the simplified product as the initial answer and not need to further simplify.

Question 2: $\frac{3}{5} \times \frac{4}{6} = \frac{2}{5}$. The numerators and denominators can be in any order.

Question 3: Either fractional factor of the product can be used for the divisor in the division equation.

Question 4: Students should mention that multiplying by a fraction gives the same answer as dividing by the inverse of the fraction.

Name Date

ACTIVITY Fraction Puzzles

1. Complete the fraction multiplication. Simplify the answer if possible.

Simplified answer:

$$\frac{3}{4} \times \frac{3}{6} = \frac{\square}{\square}$$

2. Use the numbers 3, 4, 5, and 6 to make a multiplication with a product of $\frac{2}{5}$.

$$\frac{\square}{\square} \times \frac{\square}{\square} = \frac{2}{5}$$

3. Create your own multiplication sentence using any numbers. Then change it to an equivalent division sentence. Simplify the answer if possible.

Simplified answers:

$$\frac{\square}{\square} \times \frac{\square}{\square} = \frac{\square}{\square}$$

$$\frac{\square}{\square} \div \frac{\square}{\square} = \frac{\square}{\square}$$

4. How do you know your multiplication and division sentences above are equivalent?

____

____

Performance Assessment Rubric

An Exemplary Response (4 points)

- Includes all the numbers to complete each equation correctly
- Simplifies fractions correctly
- Writes the related division equation correctly and explains thoroughly, using mathematical language, why the multiplication and division sentences are equivalent

A Proficient Response (3 points)

- Includes most of the numbers to complete each equation correctly
- Simplifies fractions correctly
- Writes the related division equation correctly, and explains why the multiplication and division sentences are equivalent

An Acceptable Response (2 points)

- Includes many of the numbers to complete each equation correctly
- May not simplify all fractions that are not in simplest form
- Writes the related division equation correctly, but may not explain why the multiplication and division sentences are equivalent

A Limited Response (1 point)

- Makes many errors in each equation
- Does not simplify fractions correctly
- Writes incorrect factors in related division equation

Mini Unit E Test Form A Name ______________________ Date ____________

Name each solid.

1. 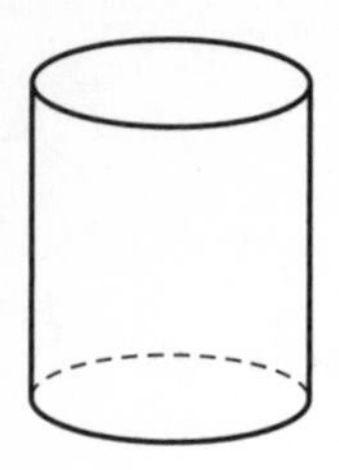

cylinder

2. 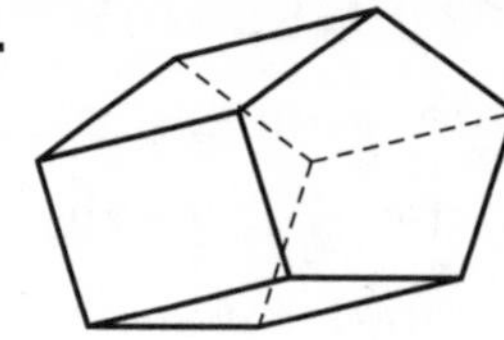

pentagonal prism

3. 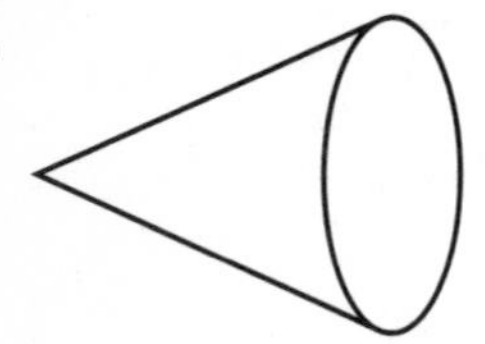

cone

4. 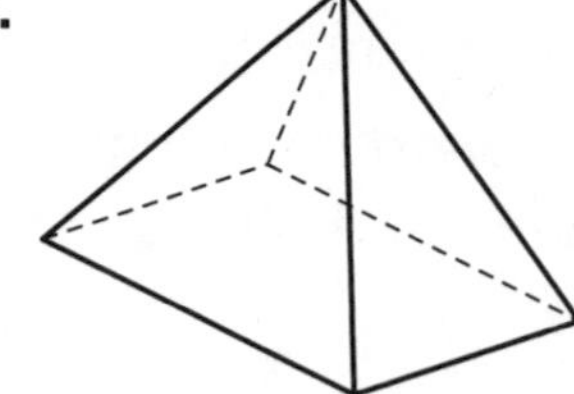

rectangular pyramid

Find the surface area of each three-dimensional figure.

Show your work.

5. 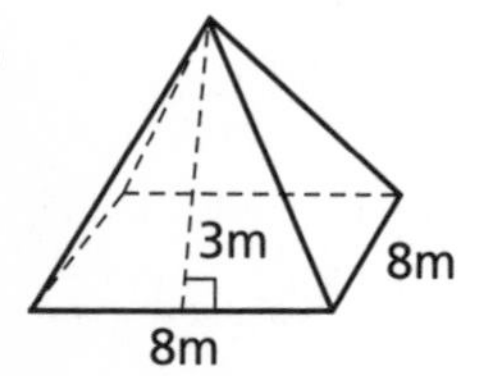

surface area = 112 sq m

6. 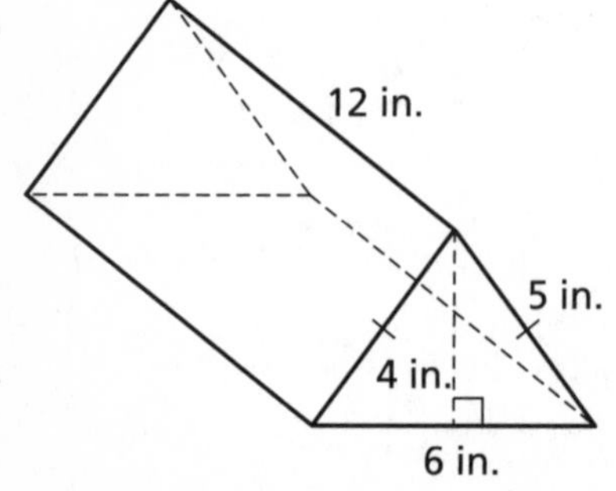

surface area = 216 sq in.

Name ______________________ Date ______________________

Name the solid that each net makes.

7.

hexagonal pyramid

8.

cone

9. Draw the top view of the stack of cubes.

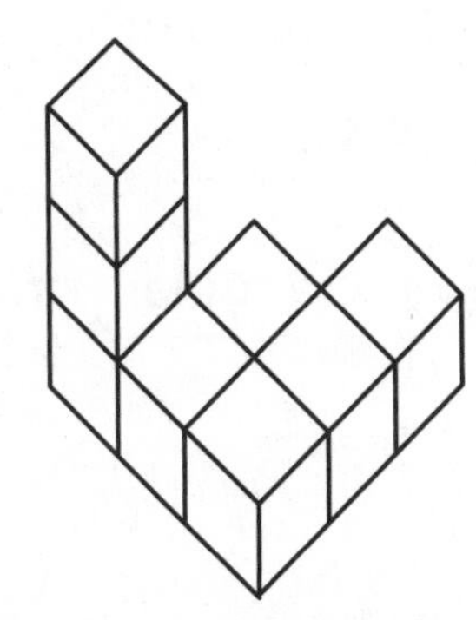

10. Extended Response Name the figure.

hexagonal prism

Draw the views of the figure.

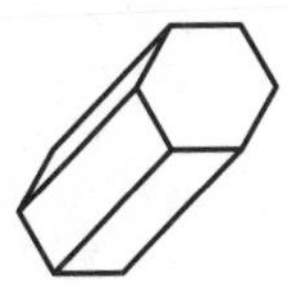

Front	Side	Top

Mini Unit E Test Form B Name Date

Fill in the circle for the correct answer.

What is the name of each solid?

1.

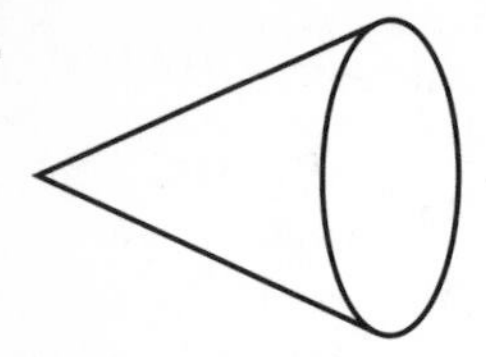

Ⓐ cone Ⓑ cylinder Ⓒ pentagonal prism Ⓓ rectangular pyramid

2.

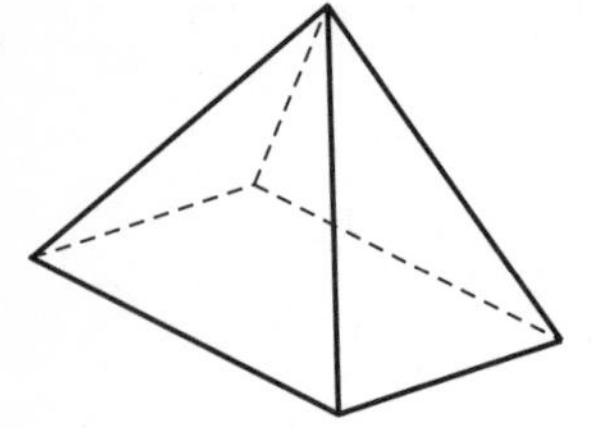

Ⓕ cone Ⓖ cylinder Ⓗ pentagonal prism Ⓚ rectangular pyramid

3.

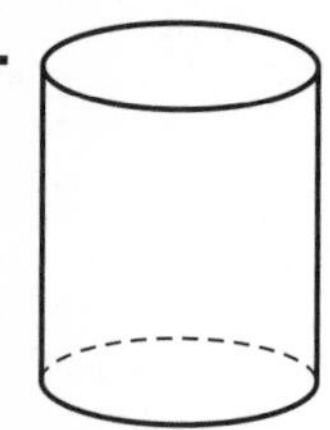

Ⓐ cone Ⓑ cylinder Ⓒ pentagonal prism Ⓓ rectangular pyramid

4.

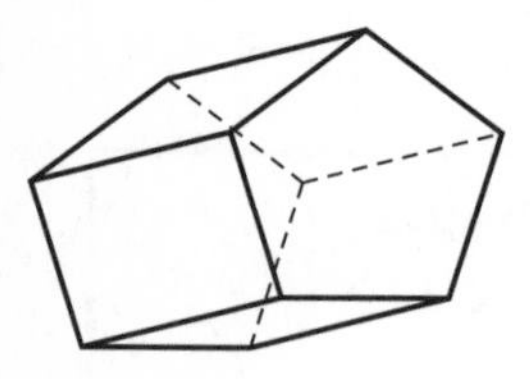

Ⓕ cone Ⓖ cylinder Ⓗ pentagonal prism Ⓚ rectangular pyramid

Name Date

What is the surface area of each three-dimensional figure?

5.

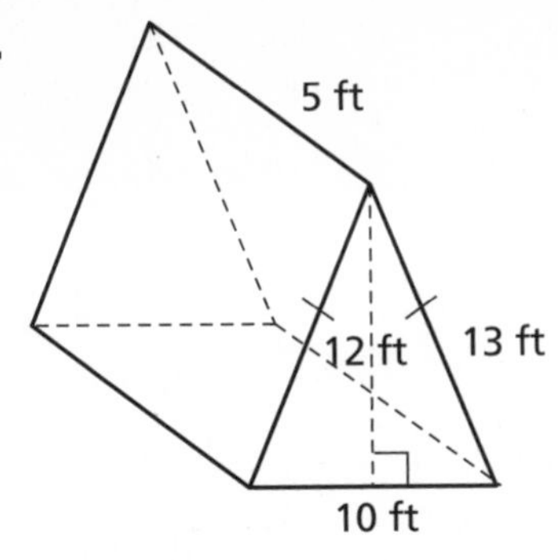

Ⓐ 120 sq ft Ⓑ 180 sq ft Ⓒ 250 sq ft Ⓓ 300 sq ft

6.

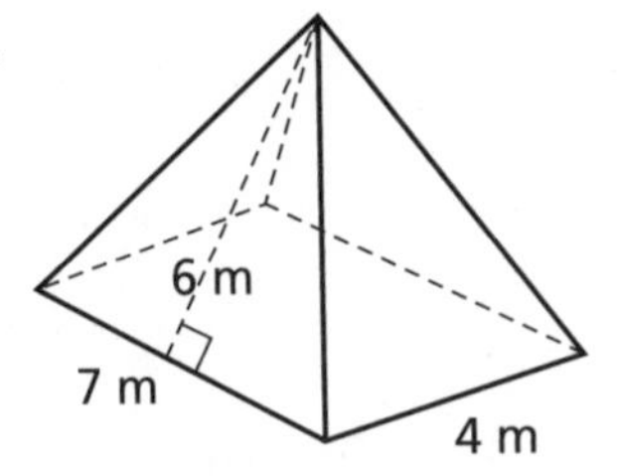

Ⓕ 21 sq m Ⓖ 76 sq m Ⓗ 94 sq m Ⓚ 112 sq m

Which solid does each net make?

7.

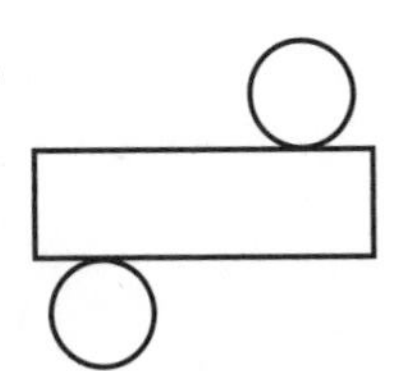

Ⓐ cone Ⓑ cylinder Ⓒ pentagonal prism Ⓓ rectangular pyramid

8.

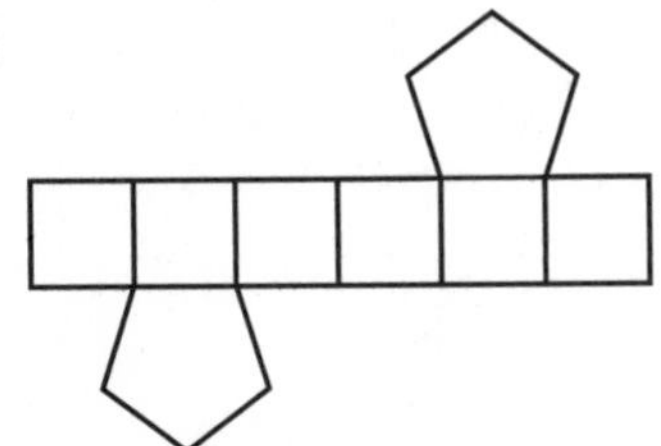

Ⓕ cone Ⓖ cylinder Ⓗ pentagonal prism Ⓚ rectangular pyramid

Name Date

9. Which figure shows the top view of the stack of cubes?

Ⓐ 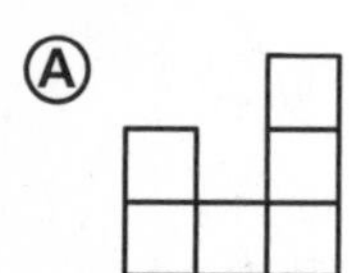 Ⓑ 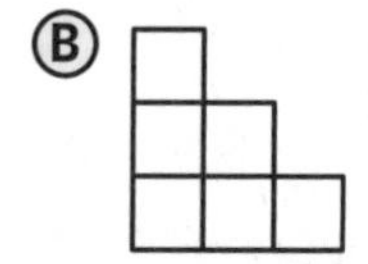 Ⓒ 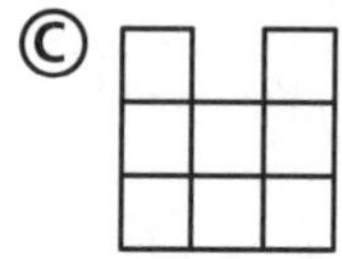 Ⓓ 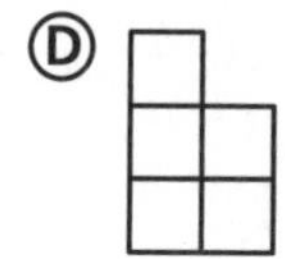

10. Which figure shows the top of this rectangular pyramid?

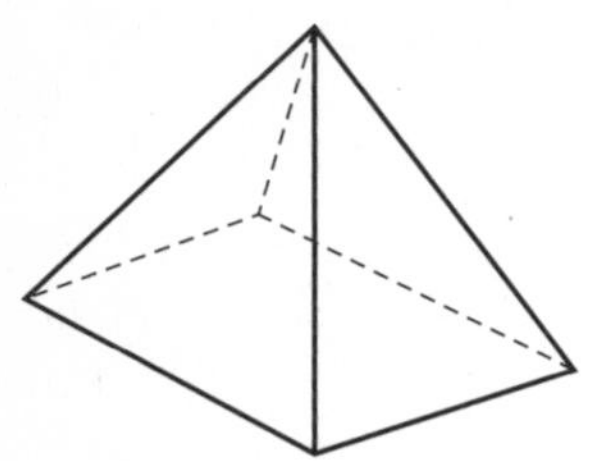

Ⓕ 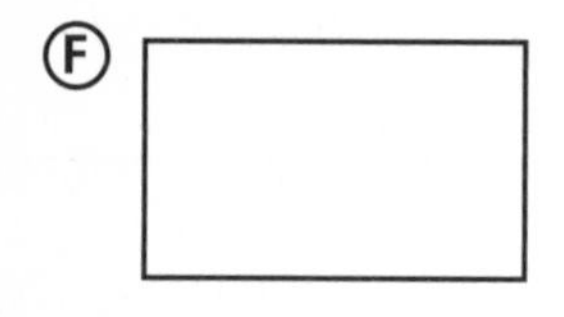 Ⓖ 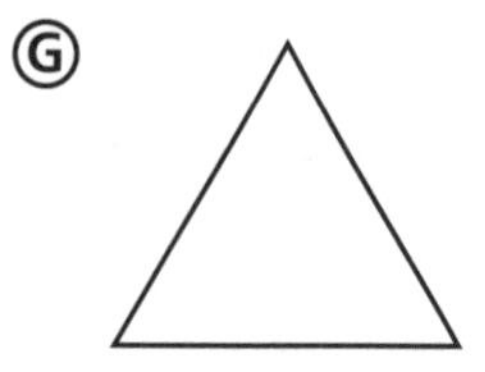 Ⓗ 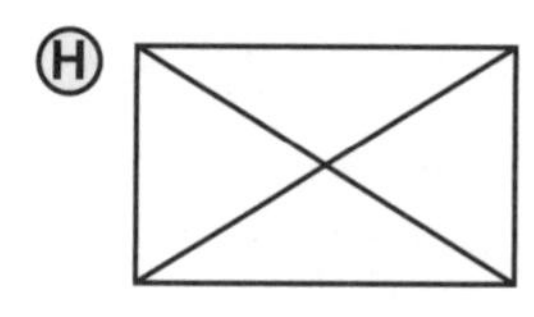 Ⓚ 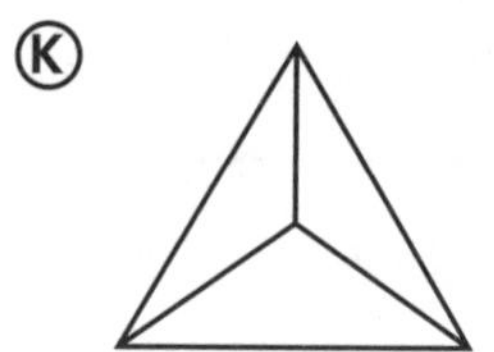

Mini Unit E

Three-Dimensional and Two-Dimensional Relationships

What Is Assessed

- Compare and contrast three-dimensional figures.
- Recognize nets for three-dimensional figures and use nets to build them.
- Find the surface area of prisms.

Materials

Centimeter ruler, paper or board at least 25 cm × 20 cm

Explaining the Assessment

1. Tell the students that they will be comparing the surface areas for two prisms.
2. Read the task aloud with the class.
3. For question 2, have them draw an equilateral triangle with sides 8 cm and measure its height to the nearest centimeter.

Possible Responses

Question 1: Both are 24 cm.

Question 2: The height of the triangle is measured at about 7 cm, so its area is $\frac{1}{2} \times 7 \times 8 = 28$ sq cm.

Question 3: Check that the student's net will really fold to make a cube without duplicating any faces.

Question 4: Check that the student's net will really fold to make a triangular prism without overlapping any faces.

Question 5: The cube has the greater surface area.

The cube has a surface area of $6 \times 6 \times 6 = 216$ sq cm.

The two triangles total 56 sq cm.
The three rectangles total $3 \times 6 \times 8 = 144$ sq cm.
The total surface area of the triangular prism is about 200 sq cm.

Name ____ Date _______________

ACTIVITY **Compare Surface Areas**

This square and this equilateral triangle have the same perimeter.

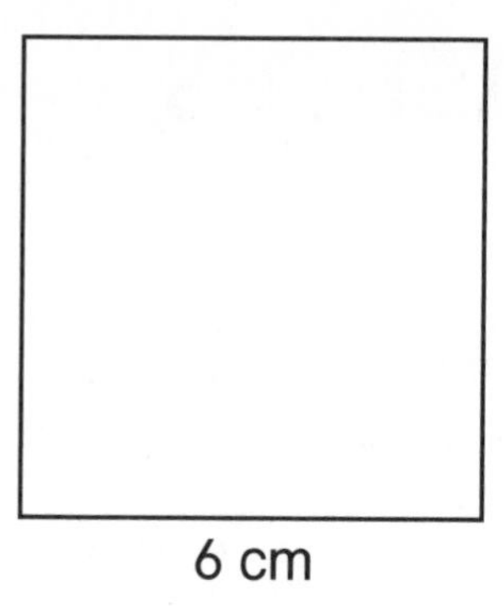

6 cm

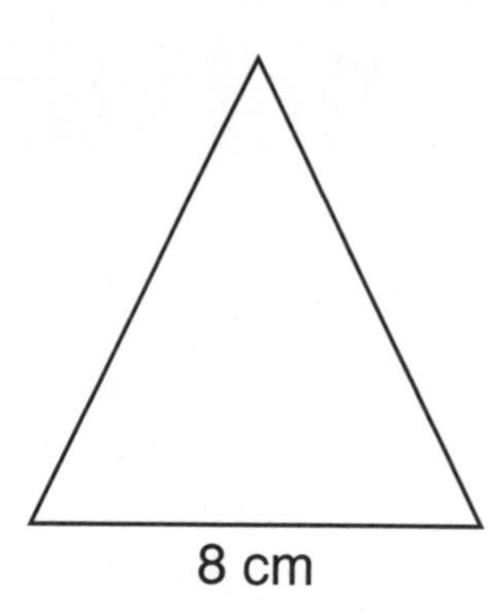

8 cm

1. What is the perimeter of each figure?

   ______________ ______________

2. On paper, draw a triangle with all three sides 8 cm long. Measure its height and find its area.

   ____

   ____

3. Draw a net for a cube with sides 6 cm long.

4. Draw a net for a triangular prism. Make the sides of the triangles 8 cm long. Make the prism 6 cm long, the same length as the cube. Mark sides to show they are the same length.

5. Predict which figure will have the greater surface area. Check your prediction by calculating.

   ____

   ____

   ____

   ____

   ____

Performance Assessment Rubric

An Exemplary Response (4 points)

- Makes a close estimate for the triangular area
- Accurately draws nets that will fold to build prisms, and that have measurements very close to those given
- Predicts the greater surface area
- Accurately and efficiently calculates the surface areas

A Proficient Response (3 points)

- Makes a reasonable estimate for the triangular area (within 10 sq cm)
- Draws nets that will fold to build prisms
- May not predict the greater surface area
- Accurately calculates the surface areas

An Acceptable Response (2 points)

- Makes a poor estimate for the triangular area (not within 10 sq cm)
- Draws one net that will fold to build a prism
- May not predict the greater surface area
- Accurately calculates the surface area of the cube

A Limited Response (1 point)

- Makes a poor estimate for the triangular area (not within 20 sq cm)
- Does not draw nets that will fold to build prisms
- May not predict the greater surface area
- Does not accurately calculate the surface areas

Unit 6
Quick Quiz 1

Name Date

1. Circle the Multiplication Column Table. Explain why the other table is not a Multiplication Column Table.

0	0
1	6
2	12
3	18
4	24
5	30

0	0
1	6
2	12
3	19
4	26
5	33

The second column in the second table doesn't increase at an even rate. The first two numbers increase by 6, then they increase by 7.

Which of these are Multiplication Column Situations? For each one:

- tell the unit and the group per unit.
- write the situation using the word *per*.

2. There are 9 plants in every row of a corn field. The field has 7 rows.

Multiplication Column Situation. Unit: row, Group: 9 plants. The corn field has 9 plants per row.

3. Katie walks 2 miles every school day and 5 miles each weekend.

This is not a Multiplication Column Situation.

4. Alton sends 3 postcards every time he goes on vacation.

Multiplication Column Situation. Unit: vacation, Group 3 postcards. Alton sends 3 postcards per vacation.

5. Make a ratio table for this situation. Be sure to label your table.

A garden design calls for 7 bushes for every 5 trees.

Ratio Table

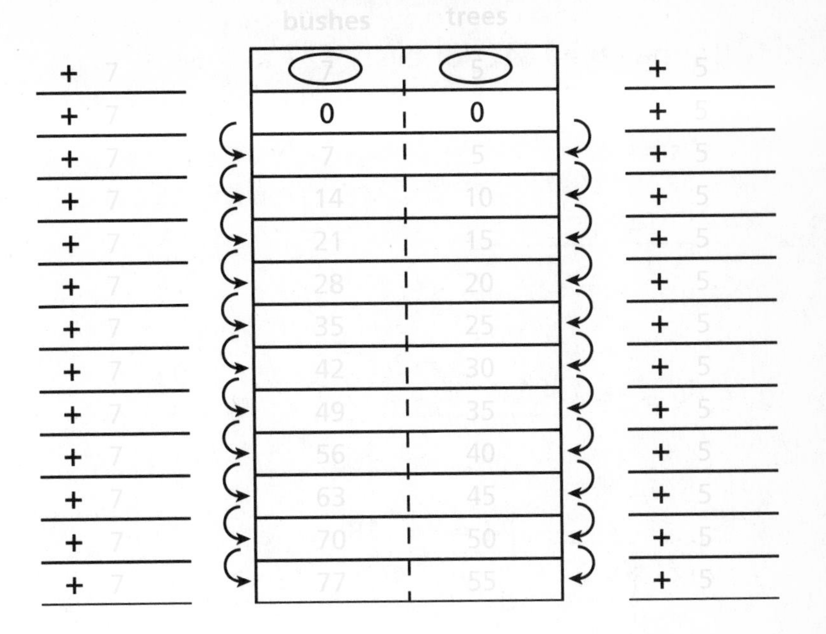

Name Date

Complete the Multiplication Table Puzzle and solve the problem.

1. Donna saved $12 for every $22 that Sal saved. When Donna had saved $30, how much had Sal saved?

$55

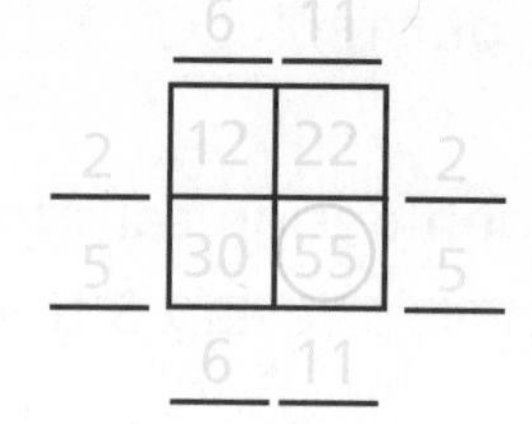

2. 6 : 9 = 10 : 15

3. 32 : 24 = 24 : 18

4. The ratio of frogs to turtles living in a lake is 4:10. 60 turtles live in the lake. How many frogs live in the lake?

24 frogs

5. A painter makes pink paint by mixing 4 cans of white paint with 7 cans of red paint. If the painter uses 35 cans of red paint, how many cans of white paint should she use to make the pink paint?

20 cans of white paint

Show your work.

Unit 6
Quick Quiz 3

Name ______________________ Date ____________

Complete each sentence.

1. ____50____ is 25% of 200.

2. 6 is ____15____ % of 40.

3. 16 is 5% of ____320____.

Solve each problem.

Show your work.

4. Heather had $45 when she went to the zoo. She spent 40% of her money. How much did she have left when she came home?

   $27 ______________________

5. A bag of 25 marbles contains 13 green marbles. If one marble is picked from the bag, what is the probability that it is green? Express your answer as a percent.

   52% ______________________

Unit 6 Test Form A	Name	Date

1. Circle the Multiplication Column Table. Explain why the other table is not a Multiplication Column Table.

0	0
1	8
2	14
3	20
4	26
5	32
6	40
7	48

0	0
1	4
2	8
3	12
4	16
5	20
6	24
7	28

The second column in the first table doesn't increase at an even rate.

They increase by 8, then by 6, then by 8 again.

2. There are 35 students in the 7 rows of a classroom. Complete this statement.

The classroom has 5 students per row.

3. Make a ratio table for this situation. Be sure to label your table.

A bead design calls for 8 red beads for every 3 green beads.

Ratio Table

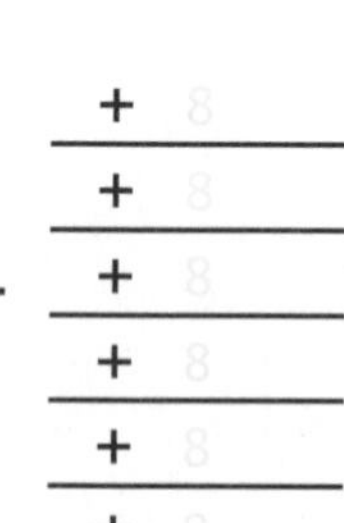

red	green	
8	3	
0	0	+ 3
8	3	+ 3
16	6	+ 3
24	9	+ 3
32	12	+ 3
40	15	+ 3
48	18	+ 3
56	21	

4. What is the value of x? $x : 30 = 28 : 12$ 70

Name Date

Complete the Multiplication Table Puzzle and solve the problem.

5. Barry earned $6 for every $14 that Tina earned. When Barry had earned $21, how much had Tina earned?

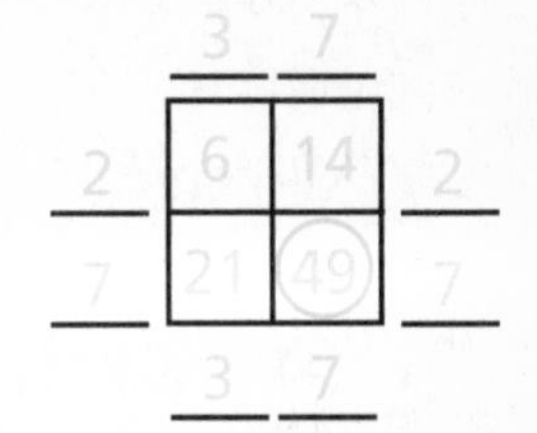

$49

Solve each problem.

Show your work.

6. The ratio of red sweaters to green sweaters in a clothing store is 7:10. The store has 90 green sweaters. How many red sweaters does it have?

63 red sweaters

7. Mr. Edwards is building toy cars out of wood. He uses 3 bolts and 6 nails for each car. When he has used 36 nails, how many bolts has he used?

18 bolts

8. Rosie had $35. She gave 80% of her money to her sister. How much money did Rosie have left?

$7

9. A bag of 25 buttons contains 9 yellow buttons. If one button is picked from the bag, what is the probability that it is yellow? Express your answer as a percent.

36%

10. **Extended Response** Write a word problem for the proportion and show how to solve the problem.

$x : 39 = 7 : 21$

$x = 13$; Sample response: Farmer Bob's hens lay 7 brown eggs for every 21 white eggs. If he collected 39 white eggs one morning, how many brown eggs did he collect?

Name ____________________ Date ____________

Fill in the circle for the correct answer.

1. Which of these is a Multiplication Column Table?

Ⓐ

0	0
1	7
2	14
3	20
4	26
5	32
6	38
7	44

Ⓒ

0	0
1	8
2	16
3	20
4	24
5	28
6	32
7	36

Ⓑ

0	0
1	7
2	14
3	21
4	28
5	35
6	42
7	49

Ⓓ

0	0
1	8
2	17
3	26
4	35
5	33
6	41
7	49

---

2. Laura has 54 red stars in 6 rows glued to a board for an art project. Which sentence is true?

Ⓕ Laura has 6 red stars per row.
Ⓖ Laura has 9 red stars per row.
Ⓗ Laura has 48 red stars per row.
Ⓚ Laura has 54 red stars per row.

Name Date

3. A baker is making cookies. The recipe calls for 8 cups of walnuts for every 3 cups of raisins. Which is a Ratio Table for this situation?

Ⓐ

Walnuts	Raisins
3	8
0	0
3	8
6	16
9	24
12	32
15	40

Ⓒ

Walnuts	Raisins
8	3
0	0
8	3
16	6
24	9
32	12
40	15

Ⓑ

Walnuts	Raisins
8	3
0	0
8	1
16	2
24	3
32	4
40	5

Ⓓ

Walnuts	Raisins
8	3
0	0
24	3
48	6
72	9
96	12
120	15

---

4. What is the value of x?

$x : 15 = 20 : 12$

Ⓕ 12 Ⓖ 16 Ⓗ 20 Ⓚ 25

Name Date

5. Danny donated $18 for every $30 that Larry donated. Which Multiplication Table Puzzle shows how much Larry donated when Danny had donated $33?

Ⓐ

	3	4	
6	18	30	6
11	33	44	11
	3	4	

Ⓑ

	3	5	
6	18	30	6
11	33	55	11
	3	5	

Ⓒ

	3	5	
6	18	30	6
15	33	75	15
	3	5	

Ⓓ

	6	11	
6	36	66	6
11	66	121	11
	6	11	

Solve.

6. The ratio of purple hats to green hats at a clothing store is 4 to 7. The store has 63 green hats. How many purple hats does it have?

Ⓕ 32 purple hats Ⓖ 36 purple hats Ⓗ 56 purple hats Ⓚ 67 purple hats

7. Gina is sorting her recycling. She fills 7 bins with cans and 8 bins with newspapers. When she has 24 bins of newspapers, how many bins of cans does she have?

Ⓐ 15 bins of cans Ⓑ 21 bins of cans Ⓒ 31 bins of cans Ⓓ 32 bins of cans

8. Jenny had $65 when she went to the carnival. She spent 80% of her money. How much did she have left after she went to the carnival?

Ⓕ $57 Ⓖ $52 Ⓗ $25 Ⓚ $13

Name Date

9. A bag of 25 marbles contains 7 clear marbles. If one marble is picked from the bag, what is the probability that it is clear? Express your answer as a percent.

Ⓐ 21% Ⓑ 25% Ⓒ 28% Ⓓ 72%

10. 9 yellow tomatoes grow for every 27 red tomatoes in Cora's garden. This season, 36 red tomatoes grew in her garden. Which proportion could you use to find out how many yellow tomatoes grew in Cora's garden this season?

Ⓕ $x : 9 = 27 : 36$ Ⓖ $x : 27 = 9 : 36$ Ⓗ $x : 27 = x : 9$ Ⓚ $x : 36 = 9 : 27$

Unit 6

Ratio, Proportion, and Percent

What Is Assessed

- Solve problems involving ratios.
- Apply unit rates.
- Solve proportion word problems.
- Solve problems using percents.

Explaining the Assessment

1. Tell the students that they will be deciding how to share the profits of an after-school business. Profit is the total money earned minus the total expenses.
2. Read the activity aloud with the class.

Possible Responses

Question 1: The total time worked is 29 hours.
The rate of pay is \$5 per hour, so the total earnings are \$145.
The expenses are \$10 + \$15 = \$25.
The profit is \$145 − \$25 = \$120.

Question 2: Tables may vary.
This is one possibility.

Name	**Hours**	**Profit**
Mindra	21	
Teri	15	
Total	36	\$120

Students may then use a Multiplication Table Puzzle to find Mindra's share.

		Hours	Earnings
		3	10
Mindra	7	21	(70)
Total	12	36	120

Teri's share is \$120 − \$70 = \$50.
The shares are fair because they are in proportion to the hours worked.

Question 3: $\frac{70}{120} = \frac{58.6}{100}$. Mindra gets approximately 59%, so Teri gets approximately 41%.

Name Date

ACTIVITY Fair Shares

Mindra and Teri do neighborhood chores after school for $5 per hour. Sometimes they work together and sometimes separately.

One month, Mindra spent 5 hours knocking on doors to line up work. Teri spent 2 hours making ads to post in the neighborhood.

They charged $5 per hour for their services.

They spent $10 on paper and printing the ads and $15 on cleaning supplies.

Mindra did chores for 16 hours that month and Teri did chores for 13 hours.

1. How much profit did they make?

2. Make a table to show the hours worked and the profits. Show a fair way to share the profits. Explain your answer.

3. What percent of the total profits should each person get? Show your work.

Performance Assessment Rubric

An Exemplary Response (4 points)

- Uses rate, ratio, and proportion appropriately
- Includes completely accurate calculations
- Considers all contributions to the effort
- Expresses all answers in correct form with units or percent signs
- Shows a proportional basis for distributing fair shares, and explains clearly why the shares are fair

A Proficient Response (3 points)

- Uses rate, ratio, and proportion appropriately
- Includes mostly accurate calculations
- Considers all contributions to the effort
- Expresses all answers in correct form with units or percent signs
- Shows a proportional basis for distributing fair shares

An Acceptable Response (2 points)

- Uses rate, ratio, and proportion appropriately most of the time
- Includes some errors in calculations
- Considers all contributions to the effort
- Expresses almost all answers in correct form with units or percent signs
- Shows a proportional basis for distributing fair shares

A Limited Response (1 point)

- May not use rate, ratio, and proportion appropriately
- Includes many errors in calculations
- Does not consider contributions to the effort other than hours doing chores
- Does not express answers in correct form with units or percent signs
- May show an arbitrary distribution of shares

Mini Unit F Test
Form A

Name ______________________ Date ____________

Is each pair of figures similar? Circle yes or no.

1.

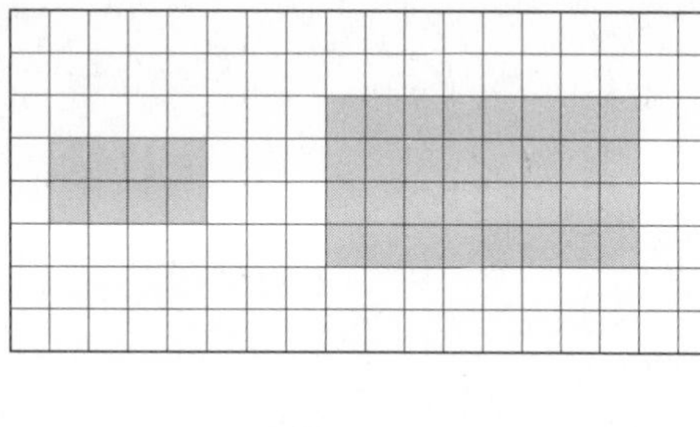

yes no

2.

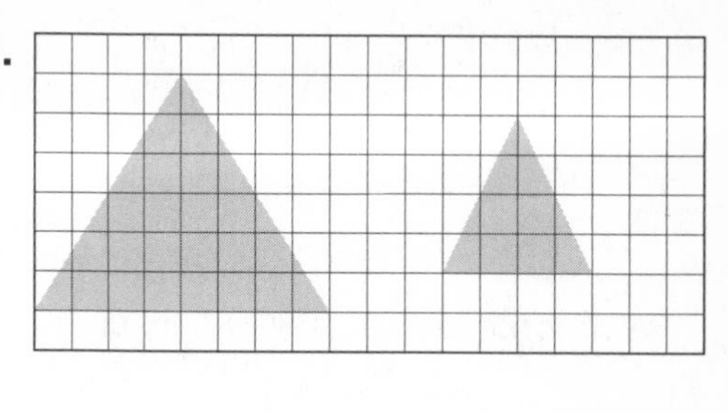

yes no

3. Draw a similar triangle with sides half as long as the given triangle.

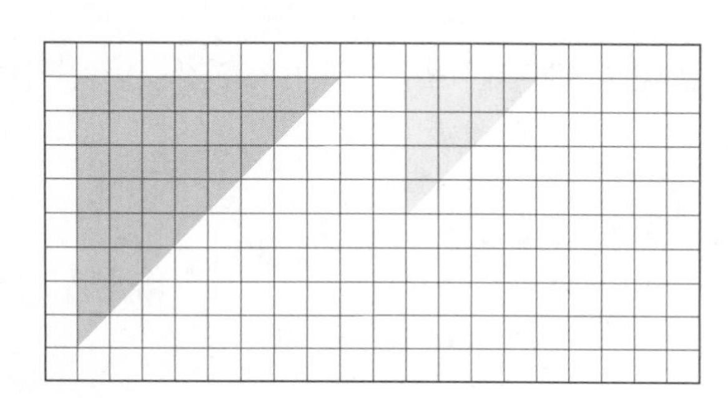

4. Write the missing measurement

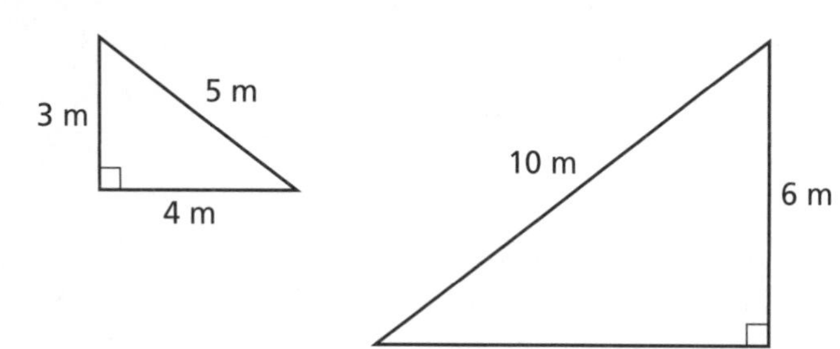

Use the scale to solve for *n*. Show your work.

5. 1 cm = 5 km

5 cm = n km

___25___

6. $\frac{1}{2}$ in. = 1 mi

$2\frac{1}{2}$ in. = n mi

___5___

7. 1 cm = 7 km

n cm = 10.5 km

___1.5___

Name Date

8. This scale drawing shows that the distance from Woodbridge to Elmhurst is 60 km. What is the distance from Woodbridge to Oaklawn?

100 km

9. On a map, the distance between two cities is 2.5 in. The real distance is 20 mi. What does 1 inch represent on the map?

8 mi

10. **Extended Response** Make a scale drawing of a room that measures 20 feet by 35 feet. Include a key.

Answers will vary. Possible key: 1 in. = 5 ft.

Name Date

Fill in the circle for the correct answer.

Is each pair of figures similar?

1.

Ⓐ yes Ⓑ no

2.

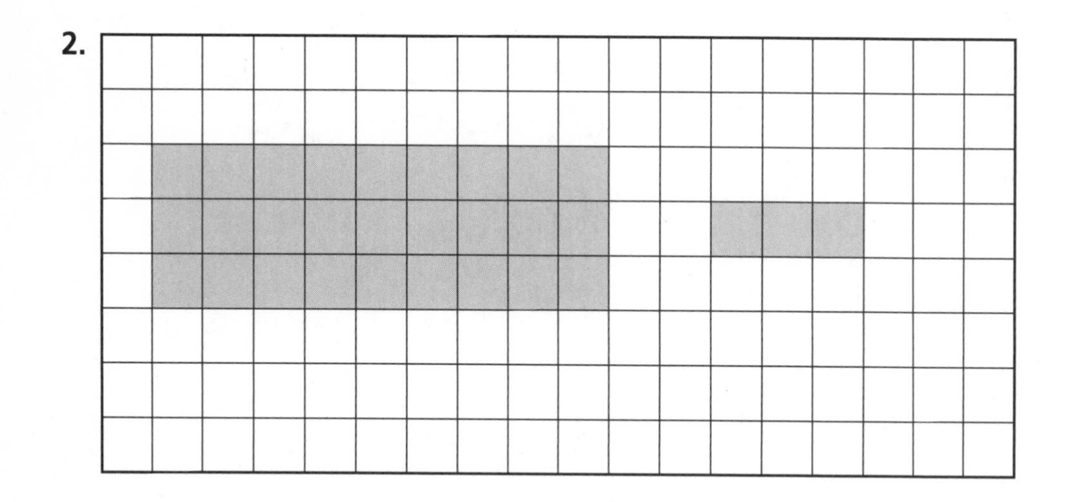

Ⓕ yes Ⓖ no

3. A rectangle has a width of 3 cm and a length of 7 cm. Which of these rectangles is similar to it?

Ⓐ a rectangle that has a width of 6 cm and a length of 15 cm
Ⓑ a rectangle that has a width of 6 cm and a length of 21 cm
Ⓒ a rectangle that has a width of 9 cm and a length of 21 cm
Ⓓ a rectangle that has a width of 10 cm and a length of 21 cm

Name Date

4. What is the missing measurement?

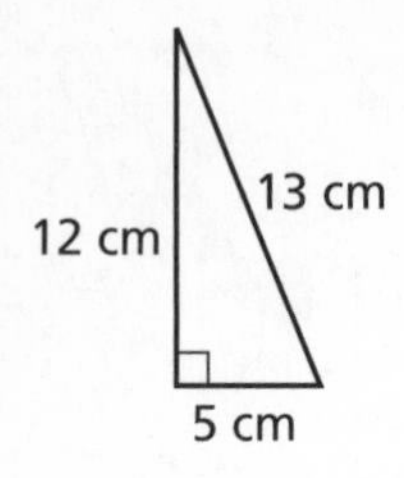

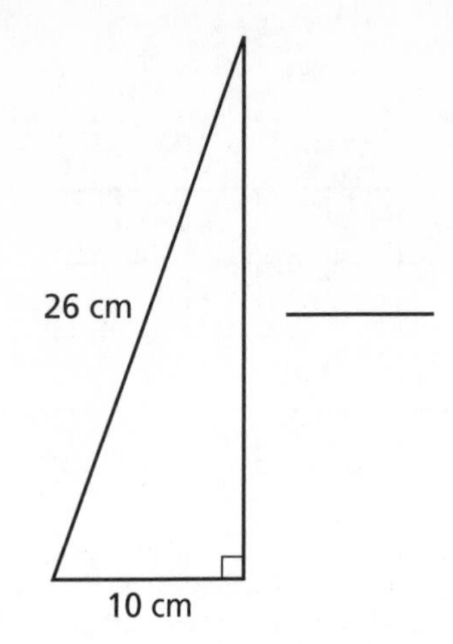

Ⓕ 36 cm Ⓖ 26 cm Ⓗ 24 cm Ⓚ 18 cm

Use the scale to solve for *n*.

5. 1 cm = 6 km
7 cm = n km

Ⓐ 13 Ⓑ 36 Ⓒ 42 Ⓓ 49

6. $\frac{1}{3}$ in. = 1 mi
$2\frac{1}{3}$ in. = n mi

Ⓕ 8 Ⓖ 7 Ⓗ 6 Ⓚ 5

7. 1 cm = 5 km
n cm = 7.5 km

Ⓐ 1.0 Ⓑ 1.5 Ⓒ 2.0 Ⓓ 2.5

Name Date

8. This scale drawing shows that the distance from Colinwood to Mayfair is 60 km. What is the distance from Colinwood to Euclid?

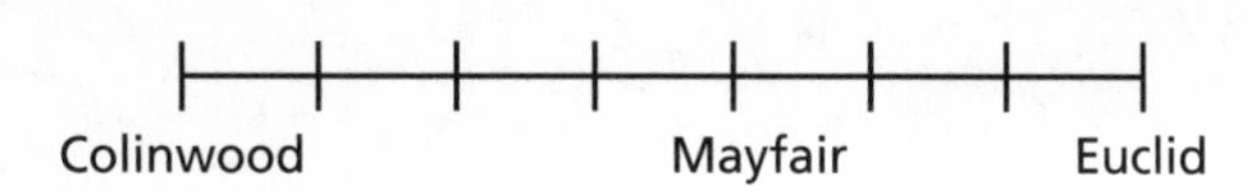

Ⓕ 120 km Ⓖ 105 km Ⓗ 90 km Ⓚ 75 km

---

9. On a map, the distance between two cities is 4.5 in. The real distance is 18 mi. What does 1 in. represent on the map?

Ⓐ 3 mi Ⓑ 4 mi Ⓒ 9 mi Ⓓ 15 mi

---

10. On the blueprint of a building, a room is 16 cm long and 12 cm wide. The real room is 36 ft long. How wide is the real room?

Ⓕ 27 cm Ⓖ 27 ft Ⓗ 48 cm Ⓚ 48 ft

Unit F

Proportion and Measurement

What Is Assessed

- Identify similar figures.
- Solve problems involving proportional relationships in similar figures.

Materials

Inch ruler, 8.5-by-11 in. paper

Explaining the Assessment

1. Tell the students that they will be finding a way to test whether two rectangles are similar.
2. Read the task aloud with the class.

Possible Responses

Question 1: The ratio can be expressed as 8 : 10 or 4 : 5 or 0.8 : 1.

Question 2: Students may draw a horizontal line to the diagonal so that it is a whole number of inches long. Then they should drop a horizontal line segment from the vertex at the diagonal. Alternatively, they can make the vertical side a whole number of inches long, then draw a horizontal line from the diagonal to the other vertical side.

Question 3: Students should show that the ratios of the lengths of the sides of the two rectangles are equivalent. One way to do this is to write the ratios as fractions and find a common denominator. Another way is to divide the shorter lengths by the longer lengths and compare results.

They might make a rectangle 6 in. by 4.8 in. and show that:

$$\frac{8}{10} = \frac{48}{60} = \frac{4.8}{6}, \quad \text{or} \quad 4.8 \div 6 = 0.8 = 8 \div 10.$$

Question 4: Students should use the same test for proportionality as in Question 3.

Question 5: Draw a diagonal on the larger rectangle. Then superimpose the smaller rectangle on a corner of the larger one. Check to see if the vertex of the smaller rectangle lies on the diagonal.

Name Date

ACTIVITY Proportional Rectangles

Draw a rectangle 8 inches by 10 inches.
Draw a diagonal in the rectangle.

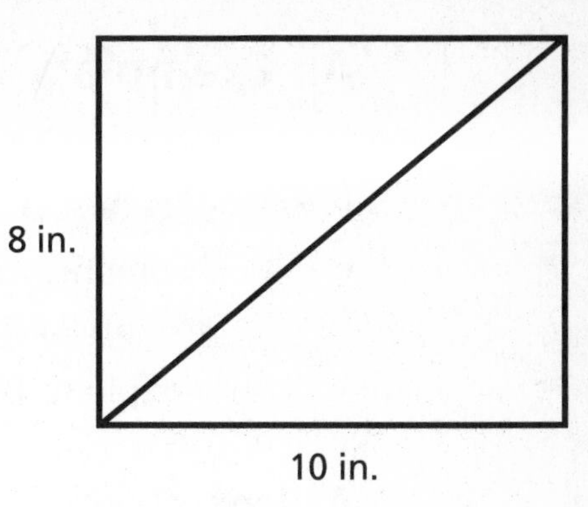

1. What is the ratio of the length of the shorter side to the length of the longer side? ______

Draw a rectangle inside the large rectangle with a vertex on the diagonal.

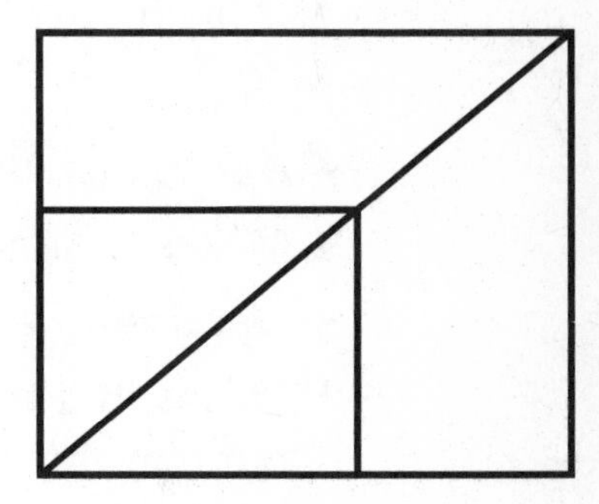

Make one side a whole number of inches long.

2. Measure the other side of the new rectangle. Label the lengths of the new sides.

3. Is the new rectangle similar to the 8 in.-by-10 in. rectangle? How do you know?

______

______

4. Draw a different rectangle on the diagonal and measure its sides. Is the new rectangle similar to the original?

______

5. How could you show two rectangles are similar without measuring them?

______

______

Performance Assessment Rubric

An Exemplary Response (4 points)

- Makes accurate drawings and correct measurements
- Identifies the rectangles as similar
- Shows convincingly and efficiently that the ratios of the lengths of sides are equivalent
- Clearly explains how to test for similarity and why the test is valid

A Proficient Response (3 points)

- Makes accurate drawings and correct measurements
- Identifies the rectangles as similar
- Shows that the ratios of the lengths of sides are equivalent
- Explains how to test for similarity

An Acceptable Response (2 points)

- Makes accurate drawings and correct measurements
- Identifies the rectangles as similar
- Claims that the ratios of the lengths of sides are equivalent, but may not show any evidence for this
- Shows an understanding of how to test for similarity

A Limited Response (1 point)

- May not draw and accurately measure a smaller rectangle
- May not identify the rectangles as similar
- Does not claim or show that the ratios of the lengths of sides are equivalent
- May not indicate any relationship between rectangles sharing a diagonal and rectangles being similar